Fifty Shades of Sunburn

By Michael McSporran

Printed in the United Kingdom

First Printing, March 2017

ISBN 978-0-9957541-0-2

In memory of our dear friend,
Phil "The Hoff" Hardy,

A man so beautiful and gentle
that God took him back early.

Acknowledgement

To everyone I have ever met in my life, be them good, bad or indifferent, I would like to say thank you. Thank you for your contributions in making me the "people person" that I am today.

A clever man once told me "there is no point in getting older if you don't get wiser" and as I travel through my wonderful, eventful life, I learn more about people with every day that passes. What makes them tick and the many ways we communicate, "You never judge a book by its cover", "You need to walk a mile in their shoes" it all makes sense now. I am always being amazed and surprised by the intense complexity of people.

It has been said that in our lives "we are not here for a long time… we're here for a good time" and I still want to squeeze every bit of fun out of whatever time I have left as I grow old disgracefully. God will let me know on judgement day, which direction I am heading in, up or down, it's probably fifty-fifty at the moment I think. I am sure God has a sense of humour and after all he made me in his image, so it's really all his fault.

In the words of the Country song "How can I get to be old and wise, if I ain't ever young and crazy?" I am going to be one hell of a smart old Man one day.

To my beautiful, caring, gorgeous wife, thank you for all the loving support and encouragement… always. I am nothing without you.

And to all the Girls I've loved before… My darling wife says "Thanks".

Contents

CHAPTER ONE

Heavens above

I gazed out to the distant horizon and watched the late sun set on this beautiful Spanish evening. The stillness and quiet calm was relaxingly peaceful and the soft breeze blew gently on my face as I watched the sun come up… what's that you ask? The sun came up? The reason dear reader the sun was coming up and not going down, is that I am at present being held upside down, by my ankles from the top floor balcony of my hotel. It seems the two steroid fuelled weightlifting gorillas who have just checked in, do not like their little love nest and like my comments about "you're here for a fortnight, it will grow on you in a couple of days" even less.

If it were not for gravity I would probably be shitting myself. "We don't like this fucking room and what are you going to do about it?" At this precise moment, I would gladly dress in chambermaids clothing and dust their Barbells twice a day if they wanted. (I did contemplate asking why they had such strong wrists!)

Whoever said being a holiday rep was easy obviously did not visit this resort.

God knows how I became a holiday rep, or to be more precise "team leader". The instant promotion to team leader was a surprise to me, although on reflection I was the sensible choice when you met the rest of the motley crew.

The school careers officer never mentioned this profession, my options were few. I did not have enough qualifications to become a brain surgeon and none of the top football clubs seemed to appreciate my talents, so it was off to the job centre for whatever I could get.

Filling supermarket shelves was a job of sorts, it brought home enough pocket money to meet my needs, which at twenty one years old were few. I had no visions of ever filling the shoes of my boss, a sad old twat who devoted his life to ensuring that the Cornflakes boxes were all in a straight line, or that no one left the building until we found out who farted during the staff meeting earlier that day. First chance I got I was shipping out.

I had spent a previous summer working as a waiter in Italy and felt I had picked up enough of the language to apply for a position abroad. I was never short of confidence to try and blag myself a job and if the lingo was a problem I would pick it up as I went along.

A friend suggested holiday repping as I had the extra language already and it looked pretty easy being in the sun all day and poncing about in a uniform. After many application forms and eventually interviews it became apparent to me that with most of these well-known British tour operators, to be a male representative did not require ten "O" levels or fluency in three languages. What would help your case was if your wrist was at ninety degrees from your arm, you possessed a voice that made Graham Norton sound dead hard and had an arse like a cooking apple. Whilst desperate for a job I wished desperately even more to stay anally intact.

Eventually the breakthrough I had been waiting for, the interview for my dream job came around. The reputation of this greatly desired post had preceded it. Sure I had heard all the stories about the orgies in the hotels, the nights on the piss the rock and roll and non-stop partying. I was sure I'd find a way to cope with drinking all day and having near naked gorgeous females throwing themselves at me and no Mother, that's not the reason I want this particular job. It's because I want to broaden my horizons, experience different cultures (and get my leg over).

My poor Mother nearly had a coronary there and then; her religious upbringing had her reaching for the rosary beads at my intentions to even speak to "those people".

"Why don't you apply to them nice people who take the crippled and sick to Lourdes and help them into the Holy water? I'm sure they'll need people with foreign languages". I said, "Mum it's not quite the same".

"Well" she spat, "at least you won't catch VD with them!"

I can still remember the right hook she gave me when I explained that would not be a problem as I could always stick my knob into the holy water instead of taking penicillin.

The prelim interviews were tough. Twelve people around the table with four interviewers, one on each corner. I quickly realized that this was a very well organized and professional company and that these "gang bang orgy" stories were probably not 100% true. Luckily I had taken the professional approach and appeared to make the right impression in the suit and tie borrowed from my fathers wardrobe. I felt even more confident when I saw one of my fellow applicants for the post, standing in his worn out Levis, with the open necked shirt unbuttoned to the waist complete with medallion and a pint in each hand, not forgetting the fag casually hanging from the corner of his mouth.

"You've got to show them you can handle your drink you know". He advised me.

I had doubts if I was suited to this job but thought that, at least I can give it a try. Seeing the competition really gave me a boost.

The afternoon was terrific, light hearted but serious at the same time.

I had never experienced such a tough interview process before. The pre interview instructions had been sent to us in the form of a letter and had told us we would be expected to stand up and "entertain" for five minutes during the group interview. This could be by playing a musical instrument, singing, dancing, telling jokes or anything we wanted. This would seem quite daunting to most people and obviously this was the first chance for the interviewers to find out if we were the type of outgoing, confident person that they were searching for.

I had been on a train from Glasgow for hours and had rehearsed my routine in my head, over and over, I was sure I had prepared myself well. After the initial pre amble and introductions we were asked one at a time to stand up and do our five minute performance. My fellow applicants had, to my surprise very obviously decided not to bother, and one at a time stood up to apologise that they did not know what to do. They were therefore given a suggested task...

"Ok you can be The Queen Mother, give us a speech about breeding corgis!"

The next one was "You be Ian Paisley and give us a political speech".

It was very entertaining watching everyone squirm their way through their five minutes of fame. When it was my turn, just as they went to announce my task, I told them that I had actually prepared something which caused a few eyebrows to raise in the room. I gave them a wee run down on my favourite subject... Me. I told them the only reason I was at their interview was because none of the other holiday companies could understand my accent, which brought a few sniggers and then I told them all about my previous (fictitious) job history. I had a list of funny jokes based around this made up career starting with my first job at Edinburgh Zoo, where my role was circumcising the elephants. The pay was shit but the tips were fucking enormous. After a short while they asked me to shut up and gave me the task of being Eamonn Andrews, the host of the TV show "This is your life", which was very popular mainstream telly on one of the limited three TV stations we had at home. (Sky TV was still uninvented in those days). The premise of the show was that Big Eamonn, our genial Irish host, would sneak up on a celebrity guest and then bring them into his studio where various friends and family would surprise them and talk about what a great person they were and relive their life story.

Putting on an Irish accent would be easy enough, but I was put on the spot and did not know what I was going to say that would be funny. There were sixteen people in the room sitting around four tables that were put together in a square, with tablecloths around them and just as I was about to do my intro to an imaginary TV camera, the main interviewer said,

"that girl over there is Miss Piggy from the Muppet show, and she can be your guest".

I looked over the other side of the table to see a pretty blonde girl with her long hair in a curly perm, which was actually a similar style to Miss Piggy and an idea occurred to me.

I put on my thickest Irish brogue and said to the imaginary film crew; "Hello and welcome to tonight's dis is your life. We have a mystery celebrity guest in the audience and we're just going to sneak over and surprise her". I then climbed under the table cover and crawled on my hands and knees around to where the blonde girl was sitting, keeping out of sight of everyone and listening to the laughter above the table as I clowned around below it. As I got level with blondie, I raised my eyes to be met with the sight of her spread eagled stocking clad legs with the mini skirt riding high up her hips giving me a very unexpected view. In my surprise I shouted out loudly

"oh fuck me, she's wearing suspenders!"

The laughter above grew to a crescendo as below the table her legs snapped together like a giant Venus fly trap and I could only imagine the colour of red, her face turned with the embarrassment. I waited a moment before sticking my head up from the table covers alongside my poor victim and in Big Eamonn's voice I exclaimed;

"Ha-ha Miss Piggy. You tought dat was Kermit the frog down dere doing dat to you, but no… Tonight...dis is your loife!"

The sound of laughter filled the room and I made my way back to my chair, silently smug as I knew I had made the best contribution so far to the day.

We had a couple of debates, with one side of the table versus the other, one team "for" , the other "against" and the first subject matter to debate was "All women should be kept pregnant, barefoot and in the kitchen." Which was easy to be "for" whilst Maggie Thatcher was running (down) the Country.

The second debate was to wind up one of the interviewers who was a Chelsea fan, in the days before they bought their titles and was titled "Capital punishment should be brought back for football hooligans and Chelsea fans".

One of the "pro" camp suggested public hangings and was countered by the Medallion Man on the against side saying,

"you shouldn't hang them, you should circumcise them… that

would soon stop them!!!"

he then looked around grinning to emphasise his well-made point and looking for our agreement.

"Sorry pal… do you mean castrate them?" I said.

"Yeah that's what I said…"

There was amusement around the room as we all realised that somewhere there was a village, missing their Idiot.

We were then moved into side rooms with the four interviewers for our more in depth personal interviews. We had some maths tests and problem solving scenarios and then it was the language test. Most of the applicants were trying it on with the qualifications and usually speaking schoolboy French or German, became fluent in both languages, the interviewer asked a few questions of me in Italian and was impressed that I could actually get by fluently. He asked if I spoke any other languages and I guessed he wouldn't test me in the others so I said fluent French and German too. Luckily I guessed right and he didn't test them, which was great as I didn't speak either of them.

I could sense they wanted someone responsible and sensible who knew how to have a good time, someone cool enough to take control in a crisis, to lead from the front. By the time said our goodbyes I knew I had a chance.

I waited patiently at home for the postman each morning and eventually the letter confirming I was through to the final stages arrived, I was ecstatic.

The final interviews would last a full weekend; we would be based at a holiday camp on the Sussex coast and be given various tasks and trials along the way. We were to meet in London if we required transport and be driven to our destination. There would be 150 people vying for around 30 overseas positions... The race was on.

CHAPTER TWO

Arrivals

The accommodation in the resort was proving to be a problem. Our "Group" type holidays encouraged the serious party animals in their hordes, and therefore the accommodation did not have to be first class. The rooms were ok if you avoided the cockroaches on the way in and as long as you did not touch the metal temperature controls in the shower you would not receive an electric shock. A sort of cheap and nearly cheerful holiday price range.

Our reps had to be available 24 hours a day and it made sense for them to live in the same hotels or apartments as the "Billys". "Billys" was our affectionate name for the guests as in rhyming slang: Billy Bunters – Punters.

We had three hotels in the resort, all exclusive to our guests, which meant the non-stop music and parties would not receive complaints from people looking for a more sedate holiday. I had two reps in each hotel and one rep looking after an apartment block we also controlled. This made up the team of the magnificent seven and so long as I could prevent them being arrested or deported, we would spend the long summer months entertaining and caring for our paying guests, keeping them from harm, ensuring they had the time of their lives and relentlessly taking the piss out of them on a daily basis.

Any problems that arose meant I would have to be involved, the team leader position meant the buck stopped here with me. I could then dilute the severity of the problem before reporting to Allan the resort manager, or Mein Fuhrer, as he was better known.

Over bookings, flight delays, lost luggage hospital visits bring it on. I was sure I could handle whatever came my way.

My outlook was simple, nothing was a problem, just an opportunity to put things right. My usual response to complaints about the rooms was "look, you're out getting pissed every night and sleeping on the beach all day. Why are you worried about your room? You only need somewhere to leave your bags, you might even pull someone and end up sleeping somewhere else." The reply was usually along the lines of "yeah I suppose you're right".

One day there was a slight panic on, when Danny the serial shagger who was my fellow rep in the hotel, told me just before I left to pick a coach load of new arrivals from the airport there was a slight problem. The twenty four new arrivals had all been allocated beds in the hotel… all except two of them! We had 150 beds available and today's arrivals meant 152 "Billys".

On the return trip from the airport I still had no idea what I was going to do, or even who was going to be left without a bed. I had left it to Danny the serial shagger to organize something before I got back, but as this was a night flight and we would get to the hotel around 2.30am it was a dangerous time to leave Danny to his own devices. The pubs and clubs would be open and to a predator like Danny, this was his time for hunting. I knew two minutes after I left Danny would be chasing some skirt and all thoughts of room problems would be lost in the tidal wave of blood from his brain to his dick.

There is always a mixed bunch at the airport arrivals, including small groups of guys and girls, couples or even solitary guests who took advantage of our single share scheme. The scheme meant if your friend pulled out of the holiday at the last moment you would be paired with someone else in the same situation and could share a twin room without being charged a single occupancy rate.

I then spotted my escape hatch, a couple of young London lads, half pissed and chanting a few verses of that well known ditty "ere we go, ere we go, ere we go."

I moved straight over.

"Are you lads looking forward to a wild time?"

"Too right mate" replied the one with the strange tattoo on his forehead.

I couldn't make out the strange writing, and it turned out it read "DAVE" only backwards as the stupid twat had tattooed himself with Indian ink and a mirror. "We're gonna drink this place dry and shag everything that moves".

I said, "I'll tell you what lads, if you know how to have a good time, don't bother checking in, leave your bags behind reception, come with me I know a great club".

By 5am they had enough, by 6am they were pleading with me to take them back to the hotel. When we arrived back just after 8am they fell asleep on chairs in reception and by the time they awoke in the afternoon we had them booked on an afternoon trip. When we returned in the evening I had sorted them a room. They never knew they had been homeless for a whole day. Funny enough they never suggested challenging me to a Whisky drinking session again.

I must mention the great efforts on Danny's behalf, he left me a note to say he was shagging a big blonde from Newcastle and therefore his room was free if it was of any use. The sacrifices that boy made for the company were astounding.

Arrival and departure days were always busy, and were planned with military precision. We could be shifting between 200-300 people in and out over 12 hours and had to make sure the right reps were on the right buses and dropped the Billys at the precise locations. Night or day my guys had to be ready, smiling and smartly dressed in full uniform giving a professional impression of the company. It was very important to the company as thousands of holiday makers and airport staff who had their own strong opinions about our set up, would have a chance to criticize us if we were less than perfect.

To be fair, spotting Stan and Shaz waiting with clipboards aloft and in full bright clean uniform at first glance looked very professional from a distance. Until you moved closer and saw the puddle under Stan's feet and watched the water from the hotel swimming pool drip from his drenched clothes on to the marble airport floor. The Billys always thought it was a hoot, to throw their rep in the pool at every opportunity.

The same pool had also caused Shaz a few problems too. Shaz was a scouser who swore like a trouper, drank pints with the boys and had shocking bright peroxide blonde hair. At least she had peroxide blonde hair until the first time she entered the pool and discovered the chlorine in the pool turned her hair a lovely shade of green!

She was rough... very rough. Once I spotted her climbing out of the pool with her hand shoved deep in her bikini bottoms, rooting around in her most intimate of places.

"Shaz what the fuck are you doing" I screamed.

"It's me Tampax, I think I've lost the Fucker, oh hang on I've found the string".

She sure was a classy lady was Shaz!

At our other hotel, Paul and Shaz had also experienced rooming problems. Only one twin room available and 3 groups of two lads arriving on different flights, at different times of the night. Nothing could be sorted till the following day. Little short arsed Brian who looked after the apartments was picking up the first arrivals, Shaz had the second lot and then Stan would pick up the third and squeeze them all into the one room. Poor Paul the poseur, the most handsome bastard in our team, would be left with the task of apologizing to them all in the morning.

I knew I could rely on each member of my staff to explain the situation with a degree of empathy to the arrivals. They would re assure them that it was only a temporary measure and then help the guests settle in whilst they introduced them to their new room-mates???… Not a chance! The bastards all dumped their arrivals at reception and scarpered.

Poor Paul, he was not looking forward to greeting the new guys and his golden brown tan almost disappeared when Stan reported that his two late arrivals were both rather hard looking skinheads. Fearing his good looks were at risk, he cautiously approached the room. It was not the most promising of starts as whilst opening the door, he cracked one of the skinheads on the skin head with it. After all to fit six lads into one twin room, you first have to remove the beds and lay mattresses on the floor. Squeezing into the room muttering apologies, and awaiting the inevitable blood bath was a brave step. The smile on Paul's face was that of a lottery winner as the heads appeared one by one from beneath the blankets and revealed that they were all skinheads. The lads were so pleased at our thoughtful arrangements to "stick all of us lads in together" and wouldn't dream of moving to another room now. Good looking and lucky… how I hated him!

Danny's problem was being anywhere on time. One busy morning, ten minutes before the coach was due to leave, Danny was nowhere to be seen. My biggest worry was that if Danny was not in his room, he could be in any bloody room. I could not exactly knock on every female guest's door at 7am asking if Danny was in beside them. Shagging clients was in the reps rule book under the section on written warnings, but I cut Danny some slack on this remembering the old adage of "people in glass houses etc". But mainly because he was the grand master of pulling birds and these birds usually had a friend for me.

The previous night I had spotted Danny in the corner of the nightclub with one of the Spanish barmaids, locking lips. I reminded him around 1.30 am that he had an airport run at 7.15 am that morning and had better get some sleep. His last words were "no problem Mac, I'm just leaving". I found him flat out at 7.05 lying surprisingly alone in his bed.

"Get up you twat, your bus leaves in ten minutes! Where is your uniform?" I searched the wardrobe for his uniform as Dirty Dan came to.

"Remember that Spanish bird from last night? Well I managed to pull her." He gloated.

"Very good Dan now here are your socks"

"We couldn't go back to hers because she lives with her parents, and she wouldn't come back here in case she was spotted." He continued.

"Marvelous Danny get your pants on." I hurried him.

"It was a lovely night, so I took her to that big park in the town centre where Allan walks his dog. I lay on my back gazing at the stars, while she gave me the best blow job of my life."

"Danny I don't fucking care, where are your shoes?" I enquired as I crouched down under the bed for his shoes, and had the stench of dog shit fill my nostrils.

"Fuck sake, I think you must have stood in something in the park."

I pulled out his shoes which were spotless, and glanced up as Danny lifted his head from the pillow to reveal the biggest dog turd in history, smeared between his hair and his pillow.

"Don't bother Danny, I'll go to the Airport" I grinned.

CHAPTER THREE

The Entrance Exam

The bus for the Sussex coast was due at 10 am in London. I arrived early on the overnight train from Glasgow and made my way to the rendezvous point. There were around forty or so people waiting for the bus, each one jostling for pole position, all wanting to organise and show how efficient and funny they were. A big six foot two Scotsman, calling himself "Uncle Bill" or something decided everyone would "chip in for a carry oot" although I don't think it was really a request. It is one of life's great unanswered questions… Whenever you travel anywhere and meet a fellow countryman and feel duty bound to have a common bond. Why do they always turn out to be an arsehole?

As the bus was about to leave "Uncle Bill" reappeared with copious amounts of alcohol for the short journey. Most people declined his generous offer to share it, I suspect it being only 10 am and on route to an interview may have influenced the decision. Uncle Bill gleefully got down to the joyous task of devouring it all by himself.

The journey was fun. A lot of good people were through to this stage of the interview and the "Craic" on the bus was great. There were a few who tried to monopolise the conversations, probably trying too hard to impress the few overseas resort managers travelling with us. Ignorance was bliss because unknown to us, these resort managers were observing every move we made and secretly taking notes.

I was quite a witty and entertaining sort of guy, I grew up with a lot of family and friends constantly joking and extracting the urine. I felt that if someone took the piss from you it was a compliment, because if they don't like you they tend to ignore you. I was trying to stay involved in the conversations, contributing one liners when appropriate. I found out quickly that I had failed to notice a shortcoming I had. I never realised that I had a strong Scottish accent. Everyone I knew understood me without any problems, then again I had only lived in Scotland and they all spoke Scottish, and in Italy I spoke Italian, as did everyone there.

Funny one liners are not so funny when people say "pardon?" or "what was that mate?" If you have to explain the joke then there is no point to making it in the first place. I realised just how strong it was, when a resort manager who came from Macclesfield, could understand me better if we both spoke Italian.

Most of the guys and girls on these interviews had probably not experienced a holiday with this group before and had the same misconceptions as the general public. From the outside looking in the job seemed like a breeze, getting pissed every night, out on the town partying, living in the sun. "Must be great being on holiday all the time?" was the phrase that I would be eternally haunted by in the future.

The next few days would separate the wheat from the chaff, the men from the boys and most probably the boys from the girls.

Not surprisingly, Uncle Bill was one of the first casualties to fall by the wayside. Our first night once we had settled in to our accommodation, and had a brief introduction to the company, we were invited to the Disco/nightclub for a party night. It was, we were told, time to relax and enjoy ourselves, and get to know everyone because the interview started in earnest tomorrow. Free drink was supplied and the club would close when we all decided we'd had enough… and of course we were so gullible and naïve we actually believed them.

The next morning the resort managers were waiting with an ambush. Everyone who had misbehaved the previous night was shot down in flames. The pissheads who never left the bar-stools, the Jack the lads and lassies who ignored all others and swapped tongues all night, and the obnoxious show-offs who wanted to be the dynamic DJ. After all, if successful, they would be working abroad unsupervised. Uncle Bill, by this time was halfway back to Glasgow, after all wetting the bed could not be tolerated, given that he might be abroad for six months and that's a lot of bed-clothes to wring out. I suppose the biggest surprise was that he hadn't wet it from the top of the wardrobe.

Over the next few days, we had to perform various tasks, like researching a nearby town and collating the information into a guidebook for the town. Then the next day giving a guided tour of the place, whilst standing at the front of the bus using a microphone. These would all be worthwhile skills in resort, when we eventually were posted overseas. Their cruellest trick however, was being invited to the cabaret that evening, only to be told four hours before it started, that our little group of fifteen people were in actual fact performing the as yet unwritten cabaret.

We sat down apprehensively to plan our fifty minute show, tried to put a structure in place and made a list of any individual talents. It was as expected total chaos, as at this point the show offs were trying to monopolise things, wanting their own individual spots and telling everyone else what to do. I had no outstanding musical skills or anything in particular, but I was never shy and did not have a problem with getting up on stage to perform.

We did the usual shit performance of miming to "Summer Lovin" from the musical "Grease" with the Girls dressed as boys in leather jackets and the Boys dressed as Girls (with very little encouragement) in borrowed dresses. A parade of "Rock stars" miming; Gary Glitter in a tinsel costume (a very popular act before the Kiddie fiddling was uncovered), Mick Jagger etc. The props were very limited, as we had to borrow most of them. We found a white lab coat and someone had the idea of putting a table on stage with a guy in the white coat pretending to be a Doctor, then we could come on stage one at a time to do some naff Doctor, Doctor Jokes. The jokes we planned were to be truthful utter shit, but this turned out to be my much-needed breakthrough.

I was still trying to be heard amongst the show-offs and managed to turn my strong accent into my advantage and turn the joke back on the audience. On TV at the time, the comedian Russ Abbott used to have a famous character called "C.U.Jimmy" a bright red haired Scotsman in full kilt with a total indecipherable accent. When he spoke you could normally understand about every one word in ten. I had a tartan scarf with me on the trip, and had managed to "Borrow" Uncle Bill's tartan Tammy before he followed the "yellow piss road" back home. The scarf would suffice as a mini kilt, and with a paintbrush tied on front I had a lovely sporran. The stage was in the nightclub where we had been set up the night before, and there were a few hundred applicants and staff watching on from the area, just in front of the bar.

The first two people on with naff jokes brought the expected groans from the crowd. "Doctor, Doctor I have a bath in milk every morning" Doctor asks "pasteurised?" "No Doctor just up to my nose". I was on third and came on, stage left in my tartan get up, marched up to the Doctor and spoke in my thickest "C.U.Jimmy" accent, until the doctor said "I'm sorry, I don't understand". As I walked off to the right of the stage, I could hear the mumble of the crowd complaining "what did he say? I can't understand him!" Two more naff jokes. "Doctor, Doctor I feel like a bridge" "What's come over you?" "Mostly cars, buses and Lorries". When I reappeared stage left and spoke in an even more exasperated state to the Doctor, it suddenly dawned on most of the crowd that they were not meant to understand me. Another two naff jokes then I paused before sticking my head around the stage curtain to be greeted by the sound of the crowd going wild, cheering and whistling. I did my bit of gibberish to the Doctor but this time kneeling down in front of him praying and pleading for him to understand me. Two more naff jokes and the crowd were chanting for me to come on. This time I crawled along the floor crying to the Doctor and handed him a board I had under my arm, before collapsing in front of him. He took the board and held it up towards the crowd, showing them the words "Where is the bar?" the place exploded with laughter and I took my bow and left the stage. Portraying the stereotypical drunk Scotsman and laughing at myself had made my impression on the crowd, instead of being on the outside trying to be heard, people now knew I was good fun and made more of an effort to talk to me and try to get to know me. It had the desired effect on the judges, as the resort managers thought it was a stroke of genius too. One of the resort managers was a fellow "Jock", who had tears of laughter still running down his cheeks, an hour after the show had finished. It seemed he too had experienced the accent problems when he first started.

The adrenaline buzz from performing on stage was addictive, the feeling of euphoria curses through your veins as the crowd laugh in unison to your pre-planned jokes and actions. The frantic atmosphere behind the curtain as everyone rushes around getting their props and costumes ready for the next section of the act. At one point my eyes almost popped from their sockets as one of my fellow interviewees, a stunningly beautiful red haired girl with an amazing figure, realized she had no time to go back to the dressing rooms for her imminent costume change. She just said "oh fuck it" and just stripped to her tiny knickers in front of me before putting on the change of clothes. Sure I had seen pairs of tits before, but this was different, this girl was a supermodel, a complete ten out of ten. She just smiled as she looked me in the eyes and brushed past me, leaving me traumatised and shaking. To this day the vision of her and that memory is indelibly scorched into my wank bank files.

I somehow got through the rest of our cabaret performance which surely had to be the one of the worst ever shows of all time. I found out later that it wasn't so much the content of the show that was important, but more that we were able to perform, react and think under pressure as well as work alongside other team members. These were the innate skills the interviewers wanted to see, because in Resort, when the immediate decisions were down to you as a Rep, you had to make the right call. No one can be trained to think that way, it has to be instinct and natural reactions. If the coach broke down on the way home from a night excursion and you were going to be stranded at the roadside for god knows how many hours, how do you stop fifty pissed up holidaymakers from causing a riot? Remember these were the days in the 80s before mobile phones and Twitter you couldn't just phone for another bus.

One part of the training had us sitting in cinema style, facing ten or so resort managers, who stared back from behind their tables on the stage. They were giving us information about life in the resorts and passing on their vast collective experience and advice. It was fascinating as to the outsider, the holiday rep is swanning around, partying, getting pissed and shagging everything within range, which to be fair is a very valid evaluation. On top of all that was that we were going to be responsible for the safety and enjoyment of numerous young thrill seekers over the summer season and play a crucial part in helping them to fulfil their holiday expectations.

Hotel accommodation lists, airport transfers, planning excursions, selling the company merchandise and trips and always getting the party started every day. We had a lot of responsibility and planning to do behind the scenes and we were going to be the selected few, the S.A.S of the holiday repping game.

During the talk, one of the resort managers pointed to one of the watching crowd and in a mock "Headmaster" style, said "are you chewing boy?" "Come here".

He proceeded to put the lad on one side of the stage and placed a "Dunce cap" on his head and made him hold a balloon in one hand and a feather duster in the other. It was hilarious, especially as it wasn't us being picked on. Another manager said loudly to the crowd "ok everyone pay attention to Steve as what he has to say is very important regarding security and banking the money you will be collecting in".

Steve, another resort manager walked to the opposite end of the stage from our "Dunce" and started talking about our safety when going to the bank carrying thousands of pounds.

I turned my head to watch and listen to Steve but out of the corner of my eye, I spotted a few of the resort managers glancing out into the crowd and scribbling on their pads. I glanced briefly over my shoulder and saw quite a few people still laughing and staring at the Idiot in the opposite corner. Again this was another very clever tactic to weed out the potential company representatives who had no attention span or sense of what should have been important priorities. I realized this whole weekend was set like an obstacle course for the recruitment process to weed out the weaker specimens.

Everyone has a mate who is the life and soul of the party who they think would make a good Rep, but could they perform with having lack of sleep, being put under pressure and put on the spot with last minute tasks and trials? These were all vital skills we would need in our armoury when abroad.

It was a bit like the X factor Boot camp, minus the shit, heart-breaking sad stories and fake tears.

It was quite an achievement to come through the whole weekend, and in fact I enjoyed it so much that even if I did not get the job, I would still have felt a glow of happiness due to the fun we'd all had. I was so impressed with the whole set-up. We were being tested in skills we would need for our new jobs, but didn't even realise it.

Sunday afternoon waiting for the dreaded tap on the shoulder and the "could I have a quiet word with you?" was a nightmare, every time someone walked behind you, momentarily you stopped breathing. Eventually they announced that everyone still sitting in the room had been selected, 33 people had been chosen from thousands of initial applicants, we were the cream of the crop.

The wait was nearly over and the joining instructions, confirmation contracts and plane tickets would soon be coming through the post. My fluency in Italian and dynamic personality meant I would shortly be chewing on spaghetti and gargling with Vino Rosso as I entertained the holiday guests.

SPAIN!!!!

Fucking Spain??? It seemed a bit odd to me that after sifting through thousands of applicants and picking the most suitable for the position they would then send you somewhere totally alien to your C.V.

After a short few minutes contemplating it, I thought, Fuck it, it doesn't really matter where I was going, so long as I was going with them. A summer season full of fun was beckoning me, the anticipation was palpable and for once in my life I could safely buy a packet of condoms without worrying that they would be out of date before I got a chance to use them.

Chapter four

The Ego Has landed

I flew out from Glasgow Airport and landed early evening in Spain to be met by Mateo our Spanish airport liaison and one of my new work colleagues. He was under a bit of pressure with arrivals and departures so we had a brief introduction to each other, knowing we would be meeting again many times in the coming months. Mateo had organised a taxi to take me to my hotel which at this point I still did not know the name of. I had glanced at the pictures in the holiday brochure but had no real preference apart from the fact I wanted one of the ones with a pool.

I made a fleeting attempt to converse with the Spanish taxi driver and watched as he stared back blankly at me, wondering what the fuck I was trying to say, which amazed me as I kept sticking an "O" or "A" on the end of every word. We drove in silence for over an hour till he pulled up at the top of a steep hill and mumbled as he dumped my suitcases at the side of the taxi then pointed down the road and sped off leaving a trail of dust.

As everyone knows, when you are going on holiday for two

weeks you take enough clothes to last a few months, my dad had commented it looked like I was emigrating for good. I loaded up my numerous bags under my arms and lumbered down the cobblestones looking for my abode which proved to be a thankless task as I did not have the address. I had worked out by its location in the brochure that it was the apartment block that we had and it included a photograph of the rooftop pool… Result.

Unfortunately because it was an ariel shot of the pool and on the roof of the building, no one recognised it from ground level. After being told to "piss off" from umpteen Spanish residents of various apartment blocks (Yes, Piss off translates into any language) and losing 10lbs through the sweat and exertion of carrying all my luggage. I realised this could be a mini crisis unfolding. The only thing keeping me going and staying positive was the fact that I had an extremely large bottle of Southern Comfort in my Duty free carrier bag and eventually I would be able to sit in my room, (wherever the hell it was), and have a drink or two, whilst laughing at the fact I had been in the country almost seven hours, it was dark and I was a pimpled, naïve and scared shitless stranger lost in a foreign country, without means of communicating or even an address to aim for.

Around 2am, at the top of a large hill I spotted a big fancy hotel with some stickers in the window of our sister companies logos, they would definitely be able to direct me. This marble oasis beckoned me to come in and be rescued and an unbelievable relief coursed through my veins. The sliding doors "swooshed" open and I entered and staggered towards the massive reception desk looking like I had just finished back to back London marathons.

I smiled my best smile at the two beautiful, gorgeous welcoming Spanish reception girls and plonked my bags down on the floor… then felt my blood turn ice cold as I heard a dull "clunk" and watched as a puddle of Southern Comfort slowly appeared under my worldly possessions.

I suppose landing in the inimitable style that I did, I should have learned to have some more empathy with my future charges. Things always have a way of sorting themselves out and a few days later I was ensconced in one of our hotels ready to welcome our new team of Reps into the resort although unfortunately minus a pool.

There were a couple of experienced Reps already in place namely Danny the serial shagger and Paul the poseur, I would have thought that with them both having more experience that they would be in a more senior position than me. A few days after working with them it was abundantly clear why they were not. Danny was an immensely charismatic guy, an instantly likeable Essex boy and an incredible performer who loved to sing on stage with his velvet smooth powerful voice. Paperwork, rules and following instructions was not really his forte, but he was like a pied piper in getting the Billys to follow him, I was instantly drawn to him and didn't realise at the time we were starting an amazing lifelong friendship. He sat me down and said "You're going to love it here Mac, the women are wild and you will be turning them down by the middle of the season." To me with my limited experience of the opposite sex, this seemed a ridiculous statement and I looked at him incredulously. "No chance of that mate, I'm sure that won't happen" little did I know how prophetic Danny's words would be.

Danny would be working with me in the same hotel dealing with around 150 Billys.

Also in our part of the resort we would be near the Apartment block which housed around 35 more bodies and was looked after by little Brian who had already carried out a similar job with one of the other "calmer" holiday companies and already knew the area well.

20 miles along the coast Paul the poseur would be working alongside Shaz the Scouser a mismatch in every sense of the word. Paul was a handsome, deeply tanned physical specimen of a man who caught the eye of every female who walked into the room and quite rightly enjoyed the attention, whilst Shaz was like a badly made up transvestite with poor taste in clothes and could probably mix it and drink with the lads more than Paul could. They would manage one of our other exclusive "Group only" hotels and look after around 120 Billys between them.

This left Stan and Kaz in charge of our third hotel which was nearby to Paul and Shaz. Stan was a good guy but if you shook hands with him, it would be advisable to count your fingers afterwards. He had an eye for an opportunity and a scam to go alongside it. If the bank was offering an exchange rate of 210 pesetas to the pound sterling. He would offer 200 pesetas and convince you the bank was not open till the following day, then at the end of the week, he would take everyone's travellers cheques and currency to the bank and exchange them for 210 pesetas making himself a tidy profit. It was nothing illegal, just a little bit cheeky.

Kaz on the other hand was an absolute diamond. Always smiling and never ever complaining about anything, you could always rely on Kaz's happy wee face to cheer you up. They too would care for around 180 Billys.

There was a certain trust amongst our magnificent seven, they were all capable (almost) of running the Hotels and apartment by themselves and we would all get together on the numerous trips and nights out we had planned for the entertainment. Alan the resort manager had already sorted a few deals out with the local venues and we had a full two week excursion package to sell, including the infamous Beach party, the Pirate Sea Cruise, Waterslide parks, BBQ nights and Reps cabaret amongst others.

In between the pre-planned trips which were mixed day and night trips, we had to keep our own Billys amused by whatever means possible and had to invent our own mini programme of pub crawls and meals out, to stop them getting bored and into trouble. We would organise an evening pub crawl and maybe approach four or five of the better bars in town to negotiate a little deal. If the bar would provide everyone with a free drink on entry then we would keep them drinking in the bar for around forty minutes to allow the bar to sell them a couple more drinks and therefore make a profit from the deal. As reps, our drinks would always be free because if they weren't we would simply take the few hundred paying drinkers to another bar where we would not be paying for our drinks. It meant we didn't have to spend anything from our meagre wages and could encourage the Billys to stay within the group where we could keep an eye on them and obviously keep the rapport and banter flowing. Stan by this time had arranged a side deal for himself to get a 200 pesetas per head on who we brought through the doors from the bar owners.

The welcome meeting we had for our new arrivals, was structured and well-rehearsed as this was very important to both the company profits and our own commission payments. The company offered cheap and cheerful basic accommodation to the masses but needed most of the Billys to book the package of trips to increase their revenue. Our basic wages as reps was unbelievably poor and we had to earn the shortfall by selling the trips and company merchandise to supplement our wages. I was never going into the job to make money, the added perks of being abroad and partying for six months was enough for me, and I don't think any of the others thought they would become millionaires, although Dodgy Stan through his many scams was accelerating on his way there.

After a few days of creativity, producing Information boards and books about the resort and activities for the reception areas, we were proudly ready for the first group of our new arrivals. The rooming lists and Airport pick up schedules were prepared and it was with excited anticipation we counted down the hours till the season began for real.

The Airport was always exciting as you never knew what the hell to expect when those arrival gates opened and having cleared customs, hundreds of boozed up excited holiday makers spewed down the corridors towards the transfer buses. This would sometimes be ten minutes after dropping a group of newly made lifelong friends who we had got to know (sometimes intimately) for the previous two weeks at the departure gate and we would have to dry our tears and fix the smile back on our faces to meet the new intake.

Having so many people moving into the resort throughout the season you tend to expect a small percentage of yobbos and troublemakers but eventually you developed a nose for it. Over the months as you gained experience as in any job, you became better at it. With the potential troublemakers, I faced them straight away to explain that if they got arrested, I would be their only hope of salvation, so it would not be wise to get on my wrong side. That usually did the trick although there were a few incidents over the summer as one would expect.

When you glanced at the arrivals list, the first thing that Danny taught me as a fellow red bloodied male, was to study it carefully and see how many "new" females would be staying at our hotel as this would be like shooting fish in a barrel for him and I, in the coming weeks.

Big group bookings strike fear into the heart of many a rep, seeing a list of twenty two names. All male or even worse all female made your sphincter tighten just a little bit more. Visions of hairy arsed rugby players tying you to the roof rack of the coach, frequently crossed your mind. One late evening visit to the Airport my adrenaline started pumping as one of the airport officials warned me a major commotion was heading through customs and all twenty six chappies were destined for my hotel. The noise and disturbance preceded them but as they turned the corner towards me, the old adage of "never judge a book by its cover" struck me.

They were hilarious, dressed in their Hawaiian shirts, kipper ties and flared trousers with the false noses and they were probably the best thing to happen to my hotel that season. They were brilliant fun, quite happy to join in with the group and get involved in all the party games. It always made the entertaining easy when you had groups of characters. I don't think their dress sense was the same when they were back home in the UK, but after spending a fortnight in their company, it would not surprise me if it was.

The big groups of Girls though??… that was scary. They always seemed to have a ringleader, who would decide on behalf of their group that they would not need to join the pre-planned excursions and trips as they could make their own fun. This was when we had to call in the big guns. We reps had a certain amount of charm and surprisingly, some of the other reps were quite attractive to women. The reps badge though was like a magnet because of the secret mysterious authority of power it brought the owner and I very proudly possessed one of them. We would call an emergency meeting of all the male reps within the area. Unfortunately more times than not, the female ringleader was usually the least attractive, fattest and unappealing of the new arrivals, and the only way to get her and her followers to book our trips and increase our commission was for one of our male reps to shag the brains out of her, and make a good job of it too. According to the plan, the next morning, the glowing faced ringleader would ask if it was not too late to book the excursion package. This caused a bit of squabbling and shouts of "it's not my turn, I shagged the last Fugly" (fat and ugly) and also put you under a bit of pressure to deliver a memorable performance that met the demands of the ringleader, no matter what it was she desired.

We usually flipped a coin to decide the loser, who would then carry out the task, although when Danny was around he would voluntarily carry out the mission. His motto was "any hole is a goal" and appreciated even fat burds need a shagging too. Whoever "took one for the team" would be excused the next Fugly lottery draw.

It didn't seem to work in reverse with female reps and Billys, but as long as we had all the girls coming along on the trips, the guys would quite happily tag along too.

We could also use this formula between the hotels in the resort to sell the trips because if Paul and Shaz had mostly males in their part of the resort, they could tell their male Billys that Danny and My hotel were full of women that they would meet on our organised trips. Sex sells and we used this enticement whenever it was needed.

It wasn't just the large group bookings that caused problems at the Airport as we found out on a regular basis. Robert was a one man demolition squad with a Tesco carrier bag full of clothes and a wallet full of pesetas.

I spotted him through the arrivals lounge, he wasn't really hard to spot amongst the three hundred or so tourists, or should I say, I didn't really spot him, I spotted the mini Union jack flag attached to his baseball cap swaying side to side through the sea of heads. He spotted me in my smart company Airport uniform, smiled a toothless smile, shouted his greetings from twenty yards away then rushed to embrace me like a long lost brother, then to cap it all, planted a slobbering beer fumed kiss, smack on my lips in front of the whole airport. The stench of alcohol nearly knocked me off my feet. A lot of people won't admit to their fear of flying and cover their nerves with one or two stiff drinks. I thought this might be the case with our young Robert flying over by himself and although he was causing me great embarrassment by singing loudly on the coach trip back, which we happened to be sharing with thirty pensioners and countless young families, I kept my composure and apologised to the passengers by promising I would be giving him a right royal rollicking about his behaviour when he sobered up.

Two weeks later on the reverse journey. A couple who had sat beside him on the arrival asked me "did you give him a rollicking then?" I reluctantly had to admit defeat because I hadn't manage to catch him sober once in the whole fortnight.

If I tried to get up at 8 am as he came down for breakfast, I would see him peering over his cornflakes with a gormless grin and a line of empty bottles of San Miguel at the side of his bowl. Trying to catch him at any other time of the day was futile. I would spend most of my evenings after rounding up stragglers from the discos, having to fish Robert out of the ornamental goldfish pond in the centre of the disco reception area. I did manage a short conversation on the departure trip, he told me he drove a long distance lorry for a living, before he passed out and collapsed onto my lap.

Robert had took advantage of the single share system which

was used by people whose friends had let them down at the last moment and they didn't want to cancel their trip, or else used by the "Billy no mates" type of guest who probably had no friends anyway. I had one of these guys who was obviously on his first ever "Group" type holiday and all the way from the Airport he kept telling me

"I'm a single share you know".

"Yes I do know" I replied after being told for the tenth time.

"I've heard all about these holidays you know, lots of girls and that yeah?"

"Yes there's lots of pretty looking girls at our Hotel, you'll enjoy your stay." I informed him…

"so which one have I got then?"

He was broken hearted when I explained he would have to share with someone of the same sex as him and we couldn't guarantee he would get his leg over during the holiday like he had been told by his mates back home.

Sharing with someone of the same sex didn't necessarily alleviate all the problems. Most people, possibly over 90% would join in with the activities and they usually committed to this at the welcome meeting when they paid in advance for the two week excursion package. This was a great deal, firstly it meant they would be involved with the main body of the group and we could make sure they had an exceptional holiday to remember and it also meant that if they ran out of holiday spending money they would still have food and drink included on most of the trips and would not be stranded back at the hotel when we were out partying.

During one welcome meeting as I scanned the faces of the assembled newcomers and made a mental note of the smiling faces and folk desperate to join in the fun, I spotted two single share lads at the back of the room. Reps can develop a knack and whilst we don't assume, we can usually place people into the type of "customer" they would probably be. Some would join in if you suggested jumping of the roof, some were needing a little persuading and some like the Fugly type needed physically persuaded to engage, and pay for the trips. We were after all becoming trained salesmen as well as entertainers.

Nigel was very well spoken and somewhat posh, obviously very intelligent, probably at Oxford or Cambridge University, but I suppose very naïve to the ways of the world. He was looking for guidance regarding the trips, towards Colin, his newly acquired buddy of all of twenty minutes. Colin was rather thin and frail with a funny walk and John Lennon style glasses and had decided that he would rather not join in with the excursions as there was plenty of architecture and museums to look at locally. Poor Nigel looked crestfallen, I could read it in his eyes, but rather than upset his new found friend he said that he too wouldn't bother with the excursions and he would go visiting museums and the like with Colin. Two days later one of my female clients was taking a romantic little walk along the beach hand in hand with a Spanish waiter at two o' clock in the morning when she spotted Nigel sitting in the sand, chin resting in his hands and staring out to sea. She had a wee chat with him and told him to explain his predicament to me the following morning and I would sort all his problems out.

He started by asking if I could move him to another room, which I couldn't because the hotel was full. He then rather politely explained that after spending two days getting to know Colin, Colin had described his deepest personal secrets including his fetish for bondage, but last night as both chums had been getting ready to bed down for the night. Colin had placed a hand on Nigel's shoulder and confessed that as well as a liking for bondage he also had a passion for homosexuality and found Nigel extremely attractive. Nigel voice squeaked "I'm frightened to go to sleep in case I wake up chained to the bed!" after almost biting through my lip trying to suppress my laughter, and offering various suggestions including "punching his lights out", I had a brainwave. I had two big loveable Irish navvies with hearts of gold staying as guests and after the promise of a nights free drinking on me in exchange for a favour, I persuaded the lads to let me leave a spare mattress on the floor between their two beds. Nigel would only need to sleep in the room, he could shower in his own room when it was unoccupied and also leave his bags there. Problem solved! Although I could picture the scene of Nigel in his Marks and Spencer pyjamas climbing into his bed that evening saying in his posh tones "its jolly decent of you chaps to let me bunk down here, how can I ever repay you?" I had visions of him sprinting down the shoreline if big Patrick put his hand on his thigh and whispered "don't worry oil tink of sometink" like I told him to do!!!

Chapter five

Trips and Good Times

There was never a dull moment on our holidays and the best time for people to come out of their shells and make real fools of themselves was during our scheduled excursions. Most tour operators would organise a quaint little bus trip to look at the local vineyards or scenic landmarks with everyone following the guide in pairs and listening to his or her every word. Our trips tended to be more than a little livelier! As I recount these stories, I am only highlighting some events from many visits to the same excursion as every trip and every group made the experiences memorable in many different ways.

One of my favourite trips was the Pirate Cruise trip, which usually started off at a relaxing pace because we were probably still hungover from the disco tour the previous night. Hangovers and sea cruises do not mix very well. With motion sickness a lot of it was in the mind of the sufferer, so a smiling Kaz used to go around the top deck giving all the Billys Smarties and telling them they were sea-sickness tablets, which inspired some miraculous recoveries.

Kaz was a real dynamo and never once during the whole season would anyone hear her complain about being tired or see her without her beaming smile, one night she was rushed to hospital with a severe asthma attack when her throat almost closed shut. The doctors wanted her to rest for a week but she signed herself out of hospital and was on the trip the next day. Concerned Billys would ask cautiously how she was feeling, and would be answered in very husky strained tones which sounded like she had been gargling with broken glass "I've never felt better in my life".

My party trick on the cruise was simple. As time was passing and I was becoming more accomplished and confident with the opposite sex and suddenly realised as a rep, I could get away with murder. I would walk along the top deck amongst the many topless bathers and announce to them that I was a bit concerned about their situation and their unawareness of the risk they were taking. Sunburnt nipple is a terrible affliction and it was my responsibility as their rep and guardian to watch out for them and at great personal expense, I had bought a solution. I then proceeded to reveal a one litre bottle of suntan lotion from behind my back and walk through the female bathers applying suntan lotion to their nipples, whilst looking at the male bathers and telling them if I had only studied harder at school, I could have got a job like theirs back home. It became a regular chore of mine and the girls would present both bosoms in their hands, laughing as I approached them. Unbelievable! The magic badge was doing its work.

I loved the cruises, not only because of my nipple protection duties but because out at sea we were in a situation where the reps were in total control. No one could escape anywhere and we could take the piss out of anyone or everyone.

With most excursions near water there was always water skiing, windsurfing and every type of water sport activity. We usually had a high percentage of people wanting to join in the water skiing although most of them were complete novices and probably just thought it looked cool. Kaz or Shaz whichever one was on my boat would go on the microphone and announce that anyone wishing to water ski should wait at the rear of the boat and pay their 1000 pesetas (around £5) to wee Brian, then after ten minutes or so, with a dozen or so wide eyed innocents eagerly awaiting their chance of gliding across the waves at high speeds. We would watch their sheepish expressions as it was explained over the Tannoy that their poor sad lives would only improve when they understood that to water ski you need to be travelling in a boat doing more than three miles per hour.

I shouldn't really mock though, I spent three years in total learning to water ski and only very occasionally did I get my arse out of the water. I must have had more enemas in those three years than all of the patients combined, in the local General Hospital.

Anyway as the cruise chugged along, after a suitable break from the festivities when most people were relaxing on the top deck sunbathing, myself and the other reps would make our way to the front of the boat obscured by the captain at the wheel.

One of the girls would take the microphone again, (somehow they believed the girls dulcet tones). They would announce that the captain had stated we were travelling around four knots and we would be arriving at our destination for a BBQ in around forty minutes. He says the temperature is around 88 degrees and ideal for sunbathing and although we are experiencing no technical difficulties, he warned us to keep our heads down for the next few minutes as a flock of low flying seagulls were approaching from the front of us according to the radar.

We could hear the Billys puzzled chatter and discussing what that meant, and as we unpacked our cartons of Greek yoghurt and spoons, they were wondering if the captain was on the Rum. We would fire a spoonful of yoghurt straight up in the air and watch as the wind and momentum of the boat propelled it back to splatter someone sunbathing on the top deck. After a few minutes of covering everyone in this stinking sticky mess, we would appear back up on the top deck to survey the damage and see everyone covered in dripping yoghurt gazing up into the sky trying to spot the seagulls. We would offer a few words of sympathy and explain the seagulls were probably too high up in the sun to be spotted.

We should really have left it at that but Kaz couldn't resist going back on the Tannoy to explain that we were past the dangerous seagulls and then suddenly scream "MAYDAY, MAYDAY we're being attacked by low flying Pigs" which was our cue to pull the same stunt using chocolate mousse instead of yoghurt.

This was usually the tipping point when the boat would make its first unscheduled stop to retrieve the reps who had now been "Tipped" overboard by the desert covered sunbathers.

We would do a bit of champagne diving with the boat parked in ten or fifteen feet of water when we would throw bottles of champagne over the side and whoever wanted to dive in and retrieve them were quite welcome to them. There were quite a few moustached, show offs in their holiday speedos trying to impressed the watching ladies as they dived head first from the top deck. Most people would nip in for a quick dip to wash off the yoghurt and chocolate mousse, but none were too quick to get back on-board from the beautiful cool clear waters. We had a little trick up our sleeves to encourage them though- we would play the theme music from the film "Jaws" loudly over the speakers and although everyone laughed and joked, they could not resist a quick glance into the waters beneath them and no one was left in the sea after about thirty seconds of the eerie theme tune.

I already mentioned I spend years learning unsuccessfully to water ski. I tried it for the first time on another water trip we had called Fantasy Island, which was really just a big reservoir that had a little desert island appear in the middle of it as the water level dropped. We would spend a day sunbathing on the island, having a BBQ and enjoying the array of water sports available. I was looking forward to having expert tuition because Paul the poseur was an expert skier and little short arse Brian had been in the Army and was an expert canoeing instructor. Wee Brian was sorting a little group of Billys to give them canoeing lessons and his favourite trick was turning the canoe upside down in front of the watching crowd and not resurfacing. While they all screamed and dived in to rescue him, he would be happily treading water with his head bobbing along contently, breathing the trapped air inside the capsized boat. It caught quite a few amateur would-be lifeguards, off guard. Paul meanwhile would be showing off on his skis. He was built like a Greek god and with his flowing curly dark locks was a handsome bastard indeed. His idea of teaching water skiing was to ski around the lake on one ski, let the rope go as he approached the island then jump onto dry land scooping the ski up under his arm without getting his feet wet, then say "that's all there is to it."

All the would-be novice skiers where somewhat terrified by this and from about twenty volunteers, suddenly there were about five, who had probably skied previously. This called for drastic action and I was elected as guinea pig by my Billys to demonstrate. I didn't have Paul's looks or physique or elegance or mahogany suntan but I did think I had good balance and I was pretty quick to learn new things. After a few brief pointers from Paul and Brian I set off floating behind the speedboat. The first few times I watched in slow motion as my skis spun off in different directions and my face plunged into the water. I thought it was quite an unpleasant sensation with the water gushing up my nose, but it was only after nearly drowning and being dragged twenty yards underwater that I realised I should have let the rope go! I did briefly get into the correct position a couple of times but I was so surprised I let the rope go to wave to everyone on the island and hit the water again, much to the amusement of the couple of hundred watching Billys.

That wasn't my most embarrassing experience on the island trip. With the other reps showing off with the water skiing and the canoes I thought there may be a gap in the windsurfing section. Stan and Kaz were both accomplished windsurfers and were very helpful teaching me the basics and with my natural balance I found I took to it like the proverbial duck to water. As I glided away gracefully from the island with riotous cheers of encouragement from the onlookers, I was contemplating that maybe I was a natural born windsurfer. It was a wonderful peaceful sensation gently floating off into that great expanse of water and Stan and Kaz had been very helpful... in fact extremely helpful... come to think of it, too helpful. Then it dawned on me... he bastards hadn't showed me how to turn around and I gazed back from about half a mile away to see them all rolling about the ground in tears of laughter. Eventually they had to send a canoe out to rescue me.

As the season progressed the water dropped again and a slightly smaller island appeared fifty yards away from our island. Most of the lads and lassies were swimming between the two and one day we nearly had a drowned Billy as one imbecile who couldn't swim tried to go between the two islands and sunk twenty feet down. Paul rescued him and gave him the kiss of life, and as we quizzed him on why he ventured out of his depth, he explained the water only came up to his mates' chest!!!! "That's because they were floating you prick!!" screamed Paul.

It was a great place our "Fantasy island" and throughout the summer months we had many relaxing trips there, although I didn't swim much in the last few months after one of my hotel guests had resurfaced from diving in and found herself two yards from an extremely large water snake that had also just resurfaced. The Billys were out the water that day, quicker than when we played the Jaws music on the cruises.

Chapter six

The Predator

It was very shortly after the season started that sex reared its ugly (purple) head. Day one of the first arrivals if truth be told, as I discovered my new exciting hobby.

I was reasonably inexperienced, being a normal nervous teenager from a small town. I was no virgin but my sexual conquests were limited and easy to remember in those days. I was used to chasing and pleading with the girls around our town and now, day one of the new arrivals and girls were approaching me?

I was like a ten year old boy who had just been given the keys to the biggest toy shop in town and I wanted a go on everything.

**(Dear Mum if you are reading this book,
now would be a good time to stop)**

I was too switched on to think that all of a sudden overnight I had become a Hunk. The other reps were good looking, toned and had deep bronze attractive sun tans but I was average looking at best. I was also pale white and l was far from stylish, Billy Connolly my fellow countryman says that we Jocks are blue with the cold and it takes us two weeks to even go white. Over the season I would turn fifty shades of sunburn, but the next day, like Groundhog Day I started the morning chalk white again.

This was a constant source of amusement to my work colleagues and I managed to scare a few new arrivals at the Airport a couple of months into the season.

"My God, where is your tan?" they asked.

"Sorry love, it's been pissing with rain for two months here" I replied.

"Oh shit, we are only here for two weeks" they yelped.

It was funny till we got back to the resort and they saw all the other suntanned reps and smacked me about the head.

It was certainly a new sensation being approached and propositioned by females. Attractive females at that. We became seasoned predators as we gained more experience over the passing weeks, but this was day one and my heart was pounding out of my chest in anticipation of what was about to happen. We didn't have to buy them drinks or meals or take them on three dates before trying to cop a feel under the bra. I just had to tell them "I'll see you outside my room at 2am" then disappear into the night knowing that they would be waiting there at the door if I decided to go back at that time. (You never know when you would maybe get a better offer elsewhere during the evening's festivities and I could move the performance to their room).

I had moved in on a little dark haired darling and it was a date and she seemed really keen too.

At 2 am the moment arrived and she was waiting as expected as I approached and nervously opened the door to my room, whilst she entered supremely confidently. I wondered should I offer her a drink or put some music on or maybe just hold hands and talk for a while, but before I had formulated my plan of attack, her knickers hit the floor beside her other hastily discarded clothes. She then turned her attention to me and had my clothes off quicker than a Gypsy removing tyres. She dragged me onto the bed on top of her and I silently prayed I could make this last longer than ten seconds.

I thought I should make an effort at romance and switched off the bedside light plunging the room into total darkness. She reached down and squeezed the iron bar I was manoeuvring between her thighs, "have you got a condom?" she asked. As a former boy scout, I was always prepared. I fumbled in the bedside drawer and found the little square packet I was searching for and thought "I fucking hope that is not an after eight mint". I tore open the foil cover in complete darkness and clumsily felt for the wet "tip" end and tried to act like an expert as I unrolled it along my now painfully throbbing shaft. It wasn't going on as easily as I expected and I suddenly realised it was inside out. I removed it and tried again by unrolling it along my two extended middle fingers. Success! Unfortunately before I had time to take it from my fingers and place it on myself properly, my impatient bed mate reached down and squeezed my fingers through the condom and immediately demanded my insertion. Aware my explanation could ruin the moment, I just kept quiet and duly obliged. In a very few short blissful minutes I reached my conclusion. Immediately she groaned "Oh no, I think the condom has burst," she seemed more relaxed when I assured her it was 100% intact as I checked my condom clad fingers and found no tear.

I wanted to run and scream from the rooftops or at least phone my mates back home to give them the gory details. And so began a season of conquests that in the interest of saving a rainforest somewhere we will not bother committing to print.

It would be safe to assume that if you played darts every day you would become a better darts player? I would like to think my experiences over the next few years allowed me to become a Cavalier amongst Pork swordsmen.

The constant practice ahead would ensure a better learning of the female body and a better understanding of what makes it play like an exquisite Stradivarius violin when it is placed in the hands of an expert.

The female psyche? Well better men than me have tried and failed to understand that.

It wasn't just the volume of women or their different shapes and sizes or their desires or turn ons….I just loved women, their softness and smell and everything about them. Pulling them as a holiday rep was as easy as trying to hit the water when jumping off the boat on the cruise trip.

With the Magic badge and its aura I just had to say "listen

love, there are hundreds of women in the resort right now and the only one I want to be with is you. My boss would kill me if I spent the evening chatting you up when I have 300 other clients to look after. Could I maybe see you later at the end of the evening?"

In the minds of the male Billys the reps could pull whoever they desired, and from the female perspective the fact that they were the "chosen one" was very flattering. Of course they would see me later. In 99% of the conversations this was the case. I would follow this up by saying "even if the boss hears about us meeting later I could get into trouble, maybe we could go somewhere a bit less crowded. How about we go to my room? I have a bottle of champagne and we could have a chat and get to know each other a bit better." Bingo! The fish was on the hook, all I had to do then was stay sober enough to finish the mission.

It is no secret that we reps were no angels and were active with the Billys, we just had to be discrete. One part of the job description stated that we had to be available to the client's 24 hours a day and I was only following instructions by trying to be with at least one or maybe two of them for 24 hours.

The reps had a competitive streak and although we didn't really keep score of our conquests we all wanted to pull the best looking girls in the resort. It was taken for granted that you would probably score with the nice ones in your own hotel because you spent the most time with them and would have more opportunities. It was therefore a massive kick in the teeth if one of the other reps got there before you. An insult like that was unthinkable.

We were as discrete as we could be and had a secret signal "Waving" code system among us to let each other know what was happening. Instead of announcing to the room "I was shagging a burd last night" you could as a nicer alternative, bring up in polite conversation in front of everyone "I had a lovely piece of chicken last night". Which alerted the other listening reps as you then casually indicated the recently acquired notch on the bedpost.

If the other reps were across the room, you would alert them by standing beside your conquest then shouting and waving frantically across calling out to them. To the watching Billys you were just waving like a lunatic to your mates. If you had achieved a sneaky stealth raid on another reps territory, you would walk right up to them and do the same idiotic wave but right in their face this time about half an inch from their nose, smiling as you watched their eyes turn black in realization of what had just happened.

There always seemed to be one especially stunning girl who just arrived in the resort and immediately had everyone's antennae twitching, Reps and Billys alike. If you were the one lucky enough to "Deflower" this prize, you entered the room doing the wave by skipping and waving opposite hands over your heels and head, like the way Morecambe and Wise used to enter the stage. It was always a moment to be immensely proud of as your fellow reps all nodded to you in unison acknowledging the enormity of this achievement.

We had a few rare arguments amongst each other, refusing to believe some of the named and shamed conquests. This brought another element to our weekly sales meetings. We started demanding proof! Evidence of your dirty deeds, we needed pictures! Again remember, this was the eighties and long before mobile phones with cameras. Nowadays you would just ask your partner to text a saucy picture and voila, it would be sent to you. We had to be a bit more inventive.

So the conversation, the sort of verbal intercourse after the intercourse would begin, "You know I'm going to really miss you when you go home and leave me here?"

"I'll miss you too" she would lie. "I would like to remember you all cute and naked, just like you are now. Would you let me take a wee photograph? It's just for me to keep and no-one else will ever see it!" They would start by smiling over the top of the covers with the top sheet held up to their neck. With some coaxing they would let it fall to their waist, giving at least a topless shot. With some silver tongued persuading, the sheets would be discarded completely and we would get a full frontal shot. I would snap away like a budding "David Bailey" and this would be the empirical evidence I needed for the sales meetings.

I did have one very keen photographic subject from Newcastle who as I lifted the camera and before I had even began suggesting anything, spun around to give me what I believe is known in the trade as "split beaver" shots.

Now the big dilemma… was it ok to get these pictures developed? Or would I immediately be placed in a Spanish prison as a budding Pornographer?

I took the undeveloped rolls of film into the local Chemist and was given a numbered slip to collect them back in a couple of days. I managed to persuade one of my Billys to nip around with the money and collection slip and I hid in the bushes across from the Hotel, watching as he returned and checking he was not being followed by undercover Police units. I was in the clear. And so began a weekly ritual of me nipping into the chemist with the undeveloped film and receiving a wink and nod of unspoken understanding from the beaming chemist, as he subtly and silently slipped the roll of film into his palm and was left alone in his darkroom with it for the next few days.

The sales meetings were carried out as normal and at the end we had a section where we could "call out" the other reps.

"you know that big dark haired piece from Rotherham in your hotel… I've been there".

"No way you're lying" they protested.

You could then throw the pictures down on the table in front of them, like a winning poker hand saying "do you want to see some holiday snaps?" On reflection we should have said "Poker"…"I did".

If sex isn't fun, then you are doing it wrong, and some of the reported shenanigans were far from romantic liaisons. Little Brian had a run in with a confident tall lady who ran her own business empire back home in the UK. She knew exactly what she wanted, and she had decided she wanted a portion of little Brian.

I personally cannot confirm or deny, but Brian reputably had a cock the size of a budgies tongue. This had earned him the nickname of Tripod in our friendly circles. This powerhouse of a lady domineered poor Brian, she picked him up disrobed him and threw him down on the bed. She approached his "massive" weapon with her mouth wide open and Brian braced himself for impact, but gripped the sheets and screamed as instead she deeply bit into the skin at the side of his shaft.

"What the fuck" he exclaimed.

She said "I like it rough" and drew her sharpened nails down the chest of a startled Brian, ripping through his flesh and leaving four thin trails of blood along the scratch marks.

"Well I fucking don't!" whined Brian as he grabbed her by the hair and escorted her out into the corridor, with them both still naked as the day they were born, he threw her clothes at her feet as he slammed and locked the door shut, then cowered behind the wardrobe licking his wounds, "still in shock".

She did make amends a few days later by apologising and begging Brian for another chance. "You can even tie my hands together, if you like?" Brian decide to finish the job and tried to give her a rough session from behind slamming her with every millimetre he had. Unfortunately it was like throwing a sausage up the Clyde tunnel.

Poor wee Brian, often as he unzipped and presented his erect member to previous girlfriends, he was asked "Who do you think you're going to satisfy with that tiny thing?" his standard answer was …."Me".

Stan also had a memorable moment of disaster. For us pulling and separating girls from their group of friends was a skilled art form, which was an acquired skill, just like a pride of lions separating the weakest wildebeest from their herd, and sometimes required teamwork. Being a wingman and taking the ugly mate from the pair was a standard easy request, but separating a pair of close friends who usually had boyfriends back home, took deviousness.

They had probably made a pact that they would watch out for each other and make sure that they stayed faithful during their holiday. Our approach was planned to perfection. The most senior rep present, usually Alan or myself would approach the girls standing at the bar and ask one of them if we could have a word in private. This was unexpected and as we were in important positions the girl would automatically comply. We would take the girl around ten or fifteen feet away from her mate to ensure we could not be overheard and strategically place the girl with her back to her friend while we addressed her.

What we would actually be saying was along the lines of "Listen, I'll wager a little bet between you and I. I bet that (in this case Stan), will pull your mate tonight". This usually brought a weak protest of "my mate is not like that, she has a boyfriend". We would continue "but you're not allowed to tip her off or stop her, I will bet you a bottle of champagne, he'll pull her".

While this jokey conversation was taking place, the intended prey was stood alone at the bar swirling the ice in her drink and staring at the floor, waiting on her mate to finish this very important discussion. This is when Stan approached her at the opposite side to her friend and ensured they now had their backs to each other. His conversation would start, "Hi there, I noticed your mate has gone off and left you alone, I knew that my mate (Alan or me) fancied her but I didn't expect him to pull her so quickly. Can I get you another drink?" She would glance around over her shoulder to see the two of us in deep discourse, laughing and giggling and automatically think that her mate seemed interested and happy to be there. In her mind she would think, "I thought she wanted to be faithful to her boyfriend? Oh well, she must fancy him after all." Stan would say "Let's move over here a bit" and guide her ten or fifteen feet in the opposite direction to her mate. Now the pals are thirty foot apart and the first girl would glance over her shoulder and see Stan and her friend happily chatting away and smiling and think "I thought she wanted to be faithful to her boyfriend? Oh well, she must fancy him after all." She would quickly realise if she stopped talking to me or Alan she would be on her own as her friend was now settled with Stan, so she would stay where she was. It would be the next morning after the deed was done that they would be blaming each other for going off with the rep first, but it was too late by then.

Anyway on one such hunting session, Stan had pulled a

beautiful naïve Welsh Girl, who was looking very cute and vulnerable in a little sexy pair of Dungarees. We ran through our usual plan of entrapment and Stan escorted her to the privacy of his room. He tried to seduce her slowly, kissing her neck and unfastening the buttons at the chest of her dungarees allowing him access to her pert breasts that he slowly feasted on. She requested the light off as she was a bit shy about her body so Stan obliged. As he tried to pull down her trouser part of the dungarees, she gave a little giggle and a playful tug of resistance, holding on at waist level as if to say "I'm not that kind of girl". Stan giggled back, he liked her innocence. He tried again and was again met with the counterforce of resistance. "Fuck this" he thought and braced his feet against the floor as this time he swiftly pulled them, leaning back using his legs to give him more purchase. The dungarees and knickers came off in one fell swoop and Stan threw them over his shoulder in the darkness and heard them thud off the door behind him. As Stan explored his young beauty with his fingers, he felt her response and was content that his experience and charisma had made her as wet as a Penguins swimming trunks. Stan introduced "Little Stan" into her body and heard her ecstatic moans as she succumbed to his manliness. Seconds after entry she asked him

"What is keeping you?"

A surprised Stan said "Pardon? What do you mean what is keeping me?"

She said "well my boyfriend is normally finished by now!" The poor girl had been dating the same lad for five years since she met him at school aged fourteen and had never been with anyone else. Obviously she thought that premature ejaculation was the normal way of having sex and what was wrong with Stan that he couldn't do it properly. The bold Stan told her to hang onto her hat as he proceeded to give her the benefit of all his experience. Stan pulled out every trick and position he knew and some he had only read about in Kama sutra manuals and proceeded to give this girl the thrashing of her life. Thoroughly spent, Stan listened to her glowing praise and amazement at his prowess as a lover and popped into the bathroom to give himself a quick shower to wash off the sweat. When he put the light on, he glanced down at his equipment and was horrified to find his blood soaked member staring back at him. One of Stan's friends had recounted a tale when he had torn his "banjo string" where his Foreskin attached to his fireman's helmet, during rough sex and it had bled for days, leaving him unable to have sex for around three months.

A worried Stan dumped his bits in the sink and hurriedly washed himself very relieved to see no tear. He re-entered the bedroom turning on the lights as he asked his partner if she was ok and found the bed covered in blood as he realized the horrific truth. "Are you on the blob?" he asked.

"Well yeah, I am" she said.

"Ah for fucks sake why didn't you say something? He demanded to know.

"Well you never asked me" was her innocent response.

As Stan realized he had not been the cause of her moistness, his eyes glanced around the room at the carnage in front of him then he spotted when her dungarees had hit the door there was a four inch smear where the flying sanitary towel had briefly connected. He would have to explain the saturated bedsheets to the cleaners' tomorrow morning and I don't think they would believe he cut himself shaving.

Chapter Seven

Hotel

I got an urgent message to get around to Shaz and Paul's hotel immediately as it was all "kicking off" with the hotel manager. I arrived to find a major commotion going on at the front entrance steps with a lot of shouting and some Spanish workmen un-stereotypically, frantically running around. The hotel manager was barking instructions and obviously trying to hurry them up.

Shaz came over to explain the situation that one of her guests, a pretty young girl with a lovely soft spoken voice called Rose from Swindon, had left a message for Shaz and Paul at reception, with Carlos, our very own version of Manuel from "Fawlty Towers". Carlos explained Rose had a twin sister who had managed to arrange a last minute visit to stay with us and had contacted our UK head office to arrange the room share with Rose and then booked her own flight from Bristol airport. Rose was en-route to the airport and very excited that her sister Eileen was coming and had told Carlos her sister would be coming in a wheelchair.

With it being in the eighties, we did not have all the health and safety controls or disabled facilities that all Hotels would need today and with our hotels being exclusively for young drunk party goers, we had never really considered we may get some disabled guests. Most of our clients only became unable bodied after our nights out and didn't usually arrive unable to use their legs.

Shaz had immediately sprang into action and had a screaming heated debate with the hotel manager pointing out it was his responsibility to make sure we could get a wheelchair up the hotel stairs. Reluctantly he had called his brother who was a local builder and very unhappy to be called off another job with his team of builders to fit a makeshift wheelchair ramp that would allow Eileen and her chair to enter the building. Spanish workers are not used to rushing and normally the manana rule applies. But today they were on a tight deadline and hence the shouting and commotion.

I did guiltily have a few selfish thoughts about how the fuck would I get her on and off the coaches and to the trips? The Waterslide Park, the beach party with all its sand and the fantasy Island, they could not have been more disability unfriendly. It would be quite a challenge but we would deal with it. I was silently quite proud of Shaz and the way she had used her initiative to arrange a ramp and after I convinced the hotel manager I would arrange a few party nights in his bar to earn enough to cover the costs, everyone calmed down. We all stood around to await the royal visit of Eileen.

Just as the workmen were packing away their tools, we saw the taxi with the girls arrive and tried to act nonchalant to disguise our welcoming committee of assorted builders, reps, Billys and hotel staff outside the hotel. Rose climbed out of the taxi beaming with pride and grabbed her sisters' suitcase from the back of the taxi waving hello to the twenty or so onlookers. Eileen, her almost identical twin emerged from the opposite side of the taxi, grabbed her sisters arm and they marched past us, up the ramp and disappeared into reception, leaving us all looking at each other in an opened mouthed stunned silence.

The silence was finally broken by the high pitched screaming of the hotel manager, directed at Shaz, Paul, me, the builders and everyone else around for miles. Carlos was dragged by the ear from the reception desk and forced to repeat the message Rose had left.

"She say she go airport and sister come in wheelchair, I swear" eventually Rose and Eileen emerged from reception ready to hit the beach.

"Rose, could you spare me a few moments?" I asked.

"What exactly was the message you left with Carlos for Shaz and Paul, word for word if you can remember?"

In her soft West Country burr "I said my sister was arriving at the airport and I was going to pick her up in a taxi... I told Carlos she is flying from Bristol cause she's coming from Wiltshire"!

It was important that the reps got on well with their hotel or apartment managers as that was the first line of defence when sorting problems. I had taken to my guys immediately and built a rapport early on although I had to educate my cleaners in the ways of the world. I had a couple of minor incidents with them early on and their first sighting of me wasn't exactly planned.

I wore contact lenses, which were a bit of a pain in the arse. I had often wakened up from drunken escapades to find out I had lost my lenses somewhere. Usually a few weeks later and after claiming for new ones on my insurance, I would find them somewhere safe, like in my smoker friends' matchbox or in an eggcup, which I'm sure must have seemed like the safest place at the time. I had pulled a bird in my hotel and was playing away at her room which was on the same floor only separated by the stairwell when I remembered I was reaching my maximum time for wearing the lenses and needed to soak them overnight. I would have to nip to my room very briefly and as we hadn't yet started the dirty deed I sprinted along the corridor between the two rooms. I quickly popped the lenses out and into their storage vessels and stripped my clothes off whilst grabbing a condom from the top drawer (just in case she demanded its presence). I bolted back the short distance, fully nude and ready for action.

We spent the night together and in the morning I realised I had to get back along the corridor in the nude to my room. It was always less funny when sober. We didn't have too many early risers in our ranks so I should be safe. I glanced out along the corridors, like I was taught in the "Tufty Club" when crossing the road, "look in both directions". The coast was clear as far as my short sighted eyes could tell, so I tip-toed along towards my room past the stairwell... only to find the whole crew of cleaners sitting on the stairs having a tea break and watching me tip-toe along in full view of them.

They were not too happy or impressed as far as I could tell. They were quite a religious bunch I think and our type of hedonistic enjoyment didn't sit too well with them.

One time a cleaner walked into what she thought was an unoccupied room to find one hungover drunk without the covers hiding his modesty and loudly screamed as she exited the door sharply. This meant that from there on, she would loudly whistle and make a noise to give the lads, fair warning that she was coming into the rooms. Unfortunately that signal just meant all the lads would whip their bits out in unison and pretend to still be asleep. You could hear her screams every morning.

With me living away from home, I would have the relatively new experience of sorting out my own washing. I asked the hotel manager if they had a washing machine I could use, to which he replied "don't worry the cleaners can do it for you". I therefore left a couple of T shirts and pairs of knickers out to be washed and sure enough, next day they were returned all washed and ironed but with a bill on the top of the pile.

Now this was no good as I was going to be doing a lot of washing over the season. I would have to sort this out straight away. One of the big perks these foreign cleaners get is that departing guests usually leave their half used expensive toiletries behind them, as they probably have extra at home. The cleaners are usually poorly paid and these luxury items are something they would not normally buy. So during my welcome meetings for the next few weeks I told all my Billys to leave all their half used toiletries with me instead of throwing them away as someone else with our group may have a use for them. Within a week my wardrobe was half full of, toothpaste, creams and potions, condoms and (unused) tampons, so much so that I could hardly open the door without it cascading to the floor. This did not go unnoticed by the cleaners who demanded that the hotel manager spoke to me.

They all gathered around me as he apologetically said, "the cleaners normally get these spare toiletries and they say, you now take them?",

" I do indeed" I also don't normally pay to have my washing done at home. So the money I save from buying toiletries will help me pay to have my washing done" I countered. A quick discussion ensued amongst the cleaners and he said "ok the cleaners say if you make sure they are left the toiletries they will do your washing for free" problem solved, although I could swear that if I took my knickers off, they were taken away as soon as they hit the floor and returned washed two minutes later. If I left anything on the floor accidentally, they washed it straight away without question. I had the odd disapproving look from them occasionally as I walked past them into my room, but this was usually explained when I found clean pair of women's skimpy knickers on top of my recently laundered pile of clothes.

My hotel manager and his wife and two kids were lovely people and I always had a great working relationship with them. It made life easier if the guests were breaking things or throwing up over the bedsheets because I could re assure them I would earn him some money by organising a party night.

Hotel party nights could be held for any excuse. We regularly had a Pool party night, in spite of there being no Pool. We would get everyone to arrive in their swimwear with their inflatables and have a little blow up paddling pool that we sat around on sun loungers.

We had Christmas parties in July and I even once had a big room party where instead of "Bring a bottle" as was the usual format, we had a "Bring a mattress" party which caused a bit of carnage. We cleared the furniture out of the room and flung all the mattresses on the floor. When you sit three or four people on a mattress and one of them moves around, the springs counteract to make everyone move slightly. When you do this with forty or more people and mattresses, when one person moves, at the opposite end of the room people start summersaulting backwards pouring drinks over their heads.

The "Boat Race" was a favourite party game with the Billys, where you would take a group of six or so people and place them in a line beside chairs and apply a pint of beer to each of them. When you finished the beer you sat down on the chair with the empty glass on your head upside down. The usual format was to play against another group, therefore we had Scotland v England or Ireland v Wales and the deal was the losers would pay for the winners' beer. The Hotelier loved this, because he would be selling twenty beers every three minutes.

I had a few tricks up my sleeve though. When my team was playing I would shout "listen to the rules of the game. You place your glass upside down on your head and sit in your seat and the winners are the first team to have everyone sitting down. Ready, steady, go…" the opposite team would be trying to quickly guzzle their beers, whilst my team casually poured the beer over their own heads, placed the glass upside down and sat on their seats. The opposite team would scream their protests and complain my team had not drank their beers, I could then refer them back to the announcement that I had just made…"I said they had to have an empty glass on their head before they sat down, I didn't say they had to drink it, did I?"

They would realise they had been had, and grudgingly pay for the beers. I would then say "Ok this time you have to drink the beer before placing the glass on your head and sitting down" This time the opposition were content that we would be competing fairly, but forgot they had just hurriedly gulped down a full pint of beer and now had to down another. The hardened drinkers could manage that but they always had a few that let them down. Back to the bar they would go to pay for that round of beers too. No wonder the Hoteliers loved me.

We had a little balcony above our Bar and dance floor area in my hotel and myself and Danny would utilise this occasionally to trick the Billys. We had a little game where we would line the Billys up in the shape of a WW2 airplane in the middle of the floor. Around fourteen Bodies standing in twos for the fuselage, two each side for the engines over the wings and maybe a rear gunner at the back. Danny would be the captain standing at the front facing them and putting on his best tinny English gentleman TV announcer voice whilst giving a running commentary.

"Ok chocks away old chaps the plane is takin orf, start engine number one" and the Billy who was number one engine would start making a whirring noise while swinging his arm in front of him like a propeller. "Jolly good engine number two is starting up now" and number two would start whirring as well. When all four of the engines were making the whirring noise and spinning their arms, everyone would lean back to allow for take-off. "Ok we are levelling out now and turning left" Danny announced as everyone then leaned down to the left to turn the plane. We would fly them around for a bit and then Danny would turn his voice into a serious tone "Oh no, number one engine has stopped" number one would immediately stop whirring and waving his arm. "Don't worry it's not a problem, these old planes can manage to stay airborne with just three engines", the three whirring engines made a more eerie sound than when they were previously four. "Oh no, number three engine appears to have broken too". Number three stopped whirring followed shortly by a mayday call as number two engine also failed. This just left Danny reassuring everyone that the solitary Engine who was whirring away like crazy on his own was enough to keep them in the skies.

Danny then screeched "Oh my God, number four engine has caught fire, HELP, HELP, FIRE, FIRE" this was the cue that myself and the three or four Billys I had roped in to assist me, would appear from the balcony above to throw buckets and buckets of freezing cold water over the whole fuselage down below us, leaving them dripping wet.

Then hotel floor would be flooded, this time with water instead of beer, and my poor friendly neighbourhood cleaners would try to skulk out of view, glaring at me as they went.

One of the favourite hotel nights was the "Miss World Competition" which was a staple diet of the British holiday camps like Butlins and Pontins. The main difference in our event was that it was the Lads and not the lassies who were to be judged as Miss World, firstly in evening wear and then in Swimwear.

This meant the girls were applying make-up and costumes all afternoon to their chosen victim including eye liners, lipsticks and occasionally Tampax earrings with the string casually placed over the ears.

We would parade these horrendous examples of trans-vestism along the stage and then interview them individually which was usually hilarious.

The delightful beauties wearing their finest evening wear were asked for their names and occupation firstly. The lads were an inventive bunch and we would have "Gorgeous Gloria" from Goodwood who was an "Erection Deconstruction Engineer" and "Delightful Daphne" from Doncaster who worked the building sites as a "Prick Layer". Don't ever let them tell you otherwise girls, Lads love dressing up as women.

After the swimwear round, which had some sights that would make you want to burn your own eyes out, we would announce the winner and "her" runners up. We would present them with full Crown, sceptre and sash and make a big fuss with glasses of champagne. We would be having such a good time in the hotel that everyone decided to stay in costume as we spilled out in to the main strip of bars later on. It was a terrific atmosphere and being such a big crowd we were getting quite a few looks and shouts of encouragement as we passed the groups of drinkers in each bar.

What the darling drag artists did not realise was that later on when they had to make their way back to the hotel, pissed and wobbling on the high heels, although most of them would have safety in numbers with the main group, the odd few stragglers would be walking home alone dressed as tarts! It was like running a gauntlet as they would frequently be accosted by drunken Spanish youths and propositioned.

We did have another little ace up our sleeves because next door to the last bar we took them to there was another tiny Discotheque that no one had ever seen before, right at the very far end of town. They would complain that we hadn't told them there was a venue they had not been to and would be at the front of the door knocking, trying to get in as the bouncer glanced out from the peephole. What we had omitted to tell them was the reason we did not frequent the place was because it was a Gay disco and already had its fair quota of weird looking transvestites. Some of our crew would spot them making their way in to the disco and say "Hey look, they are having a Miss World night too". The next morning at breakfast there were a few sheepish looking Billys and a few shocked expressions from the lads who had gained entry into the club.

It took a lot of hard work and inventiveness to build a happy, fun atmosphere in the hotel and when you achieved that sense of togetherness with everyone joining in and clearly having the holiday of a lifetime, you felt a sense of pride with your efforts. They say you can't please all of the people all of the time and there was always one or two oddballs who didn't want to join in.

I had a married couple who were a little bit more towards our upper age limit and had only booked on our holiday because it was a bit cheaper than most. They were like fish out of water really with all the mayhem that was going on around them and I sensed trouble when they had been placed in little Brian's apartment block and started immediately complaining about the accommodation, the noise, the resort in fact almost anything that could be complained about. They demanded to be moved into a hotel and in spite of me explaining over the phone it was an exclusive hotel for our young thrill seekers they accepted the move.

The first time I met the couple was around 3am, the hotel bar was closing and we had decided to have a "Toga" party in the hotel lounge and everyone had quickly stripped their bedsheets off and were all standing resplendently adorning bedsheets and sandals. This nutcase appeared in his pyjamas shouting and demanding that the sixty or so people gathered all shut up immediately because he and his wife could not get to sleep. "I demand you move them from this area now" he yelled. I had to physically stop most of the Billys from lynching him on the spot and I could sense a few tempers getting frayed. I took the decision to break the party up for that night, convincing the party goers we would recommence our mission the following night and proceeded to give this idiot a severe rollicking. How dare he!!, he had asked to be moved here and had been pre-warned about the noise having already been told this was a hotel exclusively for young singles and it took a lot of hard work for me to build this atmosphere of euphoria amongst the hordes.

Most of the party goers had shuffled off to bed already as the mood dampened and the dozen or so hard-core troops, had moved the party into one of the bedrooms at the far end of the building. The irate oddball thanked me sheepishly and enquired where they had moved the party to and then got even more irate when I told him it had transferred into room 22 where the Manchester Lads were staying. "But" he muttered "we're in room 23"...

"Tough luck chuck, you should have left us where we were" he was answered in Mancunian chorus.

I didn't ever receive a complaint about the incident but this was probably due to the fact that the "Irate customer" eventually got into the swing of our infectious non-stop party atmosphere and ended up shagging a dark haired siren from Preston as his drunken wife slept soundly in the room next door.

Chapter Eight

The Beach Party

The highlight of any holiday with the group had to be the Beach Party. The games were legendary and sometimes risqué, which had gone a long way to earning us the notoriety that we had gained with the media back home in the UK.

The "Bad" publicity was a double edged sword because every time they printed a story about the "Disgusting antics" and the "Sex on the beach" stories, although the older generation tutted and shook their heads, the younger generation who were our target audience, could not book their holidays with us, quickly enough.

I am sure shagging happened with other holiday companies but the press weren't interested in that.

If a group of four young guys or girls went away with a normal tour operator, the first thing they wanted to find out is where are the best bars and clubs to find some action and meet members of the opposite sex.

With our lot, we were all in the same hotel and on the same buses and the same excursions, so the chances of pairing off were tremendously increased.

Obviously as many people the world over have found out, alcohol can help facilitate these liaisons and can also lower your standards of acceptability when it comes to a choice of partner. Our role as reps was to start the party and get the fun flowing, mix young people with alcohol, then stand back and watch the explosion. A role we carried out to exceptional standards on a daily basis.

We would arrive at the pre-planned area of the beach in front of the beach bar where we would be having our lunch later and usually we would find the area packed with sunbathing tourists. A few minutes of our hordes sitting amongst them causing their usual commotion and they would pick up their beach umbrellas and towels and shift further along the sands to a quieter spot, leaving us a clear stretch of sand to play our games. Contrary to public belief, we rarely made people do anything against their wishes, if someone just wanted to sit in the sand and spectate as we clowned around then that was fine.

We would split the teams into groups representing their hotels and announce we needed three volunteers from each hotel or whatever we required. There were always plenty of takers willing to have a go. We had the usual running up to the wooden pole in the ground, necking a large sangria and the running around the pole ten times in small circles with your forehead planted firmly on the pole. When they attempted to sprint back to the start point, all co-ordination was gone and they usually spiralled off sideways into either the watching spectators or into the sea.

We would get the teams in pairs facing each other and they would throw a boiled egg to each other without it breaking. If successful they would move a further six feet apart and try to throw it again with the eventual winners being the pair who could throw it the furthest distance without breaking the boiled egg and catch it still fully intact. Being competitive and caught in the moment with their full concentration on their partners throw, they seldom noticed when the reps took the egg to inspect it was undamaged and casually handed them back a fully intact "un-boiled raw egg", then gleefully watched as someone attempted to catch a raw egg flying through the air towards them at great speed... SPLATT!!!

There were always a few characters in each hotel and there was always a few plonkers and sad individuals amongst the crowd who were destined to become the fall guys for the jokes.

One of the games we played was the "Tarzan" game when we would pick a "Tarzan" and a "Jane" from each hotel or apartment. Three from the four "Tarzans" would be hunky strong fit good looking young men and three from the four "Janes" would be small, slim good looking young girls. The fourth Tarzan and Jane would be the fall guys for the joke. Tarzan number four would be the smallest weediest, frailest looking specimen of mankind we could find and Jane would be the biggest fattest female in the whole resort.

As with most of these type of pranks, it was knowing how the game would progress to the end that gave us our power over everyone else.

The Tarzans would have a course to run. A short sprint along the beach first to "Bob" for apples in a bucket of sea water and then after removing the apples using only their teeth, they and their wet faces ran on to the next task which was removing a chiclet of chewing gum from a bowl of flour using only their tongues.

Now with their faces covered with sticky flour, they ran onto the next task which involved eating a plate of lettuce while doing press ups above the plate. The last sprint was into the sea where they had to swim around a strategically placed Rep, twenty yards from the beach. As they rounded the rep and headed back to shore they would see their "Jane" waiting for them and their last task was to lift her over their shoulders and run back to the beach bar where the Billys were seated and place her at the feet of the final rep who was stationed there at the finish line.

It was an exciting race with all the watching crowds cheering and encouraging their Hotels competitors to succeed and usually by this time we were joined by some bemused locals and holidaymakers watching the escapades unfold.

The Tarzans set about their tasks with vigour and determination as they tried to finish first. The race was always competitive and extremely close... right up to the point when the Tarzans swam around the rep to find their Jane awaiting. This was when Tarzan number fours facial expression would change to one of despair as he spotted his Jane and realized she was over three times his weight. The poor bastard would struggle for a few minutes before Jane would usually have to pick up her totally exhausted Tarzan and carry him over her shoulder back to the Beach bar, which somewhat amused the crowd more than a little.

We would interview Tarzan and as a tiebreaker ask him to do a "Tarzan call" which the loin clad legend was famous for. When interviewing Tarzan number four we would ask his name and what hotel he was from and then tell him that we had carried out a survey of all the previous male occupants of that particular hotel and inform him and the crowd that we found out 99% of the men surveyed sang in the shower, while the other 1% masturbated. We would ask him "Do you know what they sing?" as he answered No he didn't, we could then tell him we already thought he was a bit of a wanker. It was cruel but at least someone was talking to him for a change.

We used the same tried and tested formula on the dozen or so same trips over the season and the same tricks always had a slightly different outcome when applied to different groups of people although it was always guaranteed to be funny.

We were a resilient bunch as Reps because we had to adapt and respond quickly to whatever obstacle we found in front of us. We had one memorable and outrageous Beach Party in heavy rain, which had been concerning the Billys as we approached the damp lifeless sand. They were fearful that the day would have to be cancelled as the rain bounced down around us… not a chance! Instead we got every single one of them to leave their bags and towels in the beach bar and marched them into the sea to join us in a gigantic energetic "Hokey Cokey" in a massive circle. Five minutes later with everyone soaked to the skin, we commenced the beach party games as normal with the weather conditions becoming a fading memory as the alcohol and adrenaline started flowing.

The plan was usually an hour or so of games, then into the beach bar to celebrate the winners and have our meal, while we parted loudly to the band of guitarists and singers who regularly entertained us. This would give Danny the chance to demonstrate his amazing singing voice and Elvis impersonations and put him in the shop display window for any female from the other hotels who had not already succumbed to his charms. It was the usual drunken reverie we had come to expect from a beach party.

As we played our games we would have funny team names and different victory dances if we won a game. Like the "Dying fly" made famous by Tiswas the Saturday morning TV favourite, where everyone would lie on their backs waving all four limbs in the air making a buzzing sound. With our hotel resembling a graveyard we would usually have some sort of Zombie name and do a "Monster Mash" if we won. Michael Jackson the child friendly singer had his famous "Thriller" song and video out around that time and we would mimic this dance with the team captain and Reps at the front with the rest of the Hotels "Living Dead" behind which was a sight to behold.

At one beach rparty little Brian the short arse and his team were finishing last in every game but loudly celebrating the fact??? Ingeniously Brian had a cunning plan and had decided that as they had the smallest numbers and probably the weakest team, they would attempt a world's first... of trying to "lose" the beach party. This way if they lost, they were actually achieving what they had set out to do and therefore by default had actually won, this was obviously a cause for celebrating. What a legend was Wee Brian.

At the Beach Bar there was a beautiful glass display cabinet with an amazing array of colourful fresh fish around a magnificent Giant Crab centrepiece, which lay framed by a thick layer of crushed ice as a chilled background. Somewhere in my mischievous mind, I thought it would be hilarious to steal this massive crab and place it inside my swimming trunks, then I could casually saunter around the tables and tell the Billys I thought I was suffering from crabs as I gave my groin a scratch and produced the biggest crab they had ever seen from my speedos. What a hoot.

I approached the back of the display cabinet between the gaps of the waiters disappearing out of view and after quickly surveying the room for watching eyes I removed the back of the cabinet. A few moments later as the waiters disappeared from view again I lifted the surprisingly heavy crab with one hand around his claw and pulled open my trunks with my other hand still carefully scanning the room for prying eyes. As I lowered the crab slowly into my trunks I got the fright of my life as the bastard crab attempted to castrate me with his other claw.

I screamed as I dropped-kicked the crab away from me, hurting my foot in the process as I scrambled backwards away from the cabinet and the lethal crustacean. How was I to know that he was alive and the ice was the only thing keeping him subdued and inanimate?

I didn't have a lot in the front of my trunks but it was all mine and in perfect working order. I was very proud of it and thank god I still had it intact for the rest of the summer season ahead. One of my fellow Reps advised me that "Them crabs can take your fingers clean off with those claws you know?"

The party was in full flow as Danny took the microphone, he soon had them rocking in the aisles as he belted out his repertoire of party songs; "Hi Ho silver lining", "Jailhouse Rock", "Living Doll" and "All shook up". The boy could sure sing. The crowd were loving it and I slipped over beside him and as he finished yet another fans favourite I whispered "Danny we've had a request from a big group of girls, could you do an Elvis version of "Can't help falling in love with you"?

He looked at me incredulously. "A slow song… At a Beach Party? …Really?".

"It's what the crowd want mate, I'm afraid" I replied.

The music started slow and you could hear a pin drop as Danny poured his heart and soul into an emotional rendition… "Wise men say… only fools rush in…but I can't help…" it was like Elvis himself had graced our presence. Unbeknown to Danny I had already asked a favour of seventy or so females from the Hotels and as Danny glanced upwards in the middle of the song, I gave my signal and watched as seventy pairs of spare knickers flew through the air and landed on his head, shoulders ears and microphone as the girls screamed in unison in their high pitched voices "Elvis, Elvis". Danny collapsed with laughter and to this day, he still cannot sing that song without grinning and furtively scanning the room.

We always had fun, even when things weren't going to plan because no one except us reps would know it. There was one very memorable day that involved a disaster but surprisingly it was not caused by us. We had spent around five hours in the sun in an absolute heatwave enjoying the party and with everyone tired, pissed up and mostly wasted we started to round our charges up to get them on the buses to return back to base. As we approached the car park there seemed to be a lot of people and a lot of commotion occurring, as one by one I watched our empty coaches drive hurriedly out of the car park. Shaz ran over to tell me that there was a forest fire a couple of miles along the road from us and there were people trapped behind thirty foot high flames. The fire service had commandeered our buses and were driving them to the rescue as their hoses doused the buses with water to get access through the flames.

It was testament to the braveness of these fireman and bus drivers that no one was seriously hurt or died and it was a successful mission accomplished.

Unfortunately the buses would be gone for unlimited hours

and I still had 300 or so pissed up young party goers to babysit.

We took the decision to head back down to the beach bar and removed all the chairs from the bar and made our own imaginary buses in the middle of the sand with the chairs lined up like they were on our buses. For the next few hours we sat in our chairs and sang and laughed while the more reserved British tourists sat around moaning and whining about being left stranded and would be writing a strong letter to their MPs when they got home. We played for the next couple of hours, throwing people off the buses for smoking or farting and laughed as they stood by our imaginary bus steps for ages, begging to be let back on. We did a "Bullshit Tour" where the reps would give out facts and information about the resort and surrounding areas which were not always true and they could call us out at any point by shouting "Bullshit". If they got it wrong however they got thrown off the imaginary bus for a while. We would play against the other buses by making a chain of clothes which as we were dressed in beach attire usually meant a few of the girls going topless and sometimes both the girls and boys going bottomless, depending on how badly you wanted the victory. Now that would give the watching polite British tourists a letter worth writing. When the buses eventually returned, no one wanted to leave.

With the whole island panicking about potential earthquakes due to the heatwave, the local residents were somewhat on edge. Old people had been going to bed at night and dehydrating due to the intense heat and there were some decent earthquakes happening up and down the Island. The mini earthquakes or more accurate "earth tremors" felt like the road shaking when a big articulated lorry drove passed you. It was noticeable to us but we just shrugged and carried on our merry way. The locals however, took it as a sign that Armageddon was happening and were running from buildings onto the street or diving outside via open windows or doors. It was quite funny to watch as a few of them actually got hit with cars as they escaped their perceived site of danger.

As usual I spotted an opportunity for a little wind up and instructed all of the Billys going out on that nights pub crawl, that there was going to be a big earthquake at nine o clock precisely, that very evening. One of them asked me "how can you be so sure of the precise moment of the earthquake Mac, are the reports that accurate?"

The reason I am sure of the time dear Billy is because we are going to start it. I made sure that at precisely nine pm every one of my holiday makers in the bar, rattled and shook the tables, beer glasses and lights with as much noise and vigour as they could, and laughed heartily as the local Spanish population dived out of doors and windows running screaming into the streets as their life as they knew it was about to end. We managed to create an "earthquake" at all six bars we visited that night.

Chapter Nine

Brits Abroad

We all let our hair down somewhat when we go on holiday and being abroad where no one knows you or cares what you do, seems like a licence to go crazy. When you have crowds of young thrill seekers full of hormones and excess alcohol, anything could and probably would happen. No-one apart from their travelling companions would know what happened, "What goes on tour, stays on tour" and no parents, partners or locals in their home town would be able to judge them or gossip. It was an opportunity to act out of character just because you could and unless you ended up with a bad tattoo or STD or worse as a memento to take home then you would only have the memories of a great holiday or a guilty conscience to cope with.

Danny once described it very eloquently that we got to know the "Real them", the "I can get away with this" them. The "Them" that even their closest friends had never really know.

It was after one of our drunken Beach parties that I got together with a little Blonde bundle who eventually became my first wife after she ravished me on the bus back to the Hotel. I found out much too late that this was her "out of character" moment as I recall that was the only bloody time she ravished me.

When one uses the phrase "my first wife" it often begs the question "How many wives have you had?" to which my standard reply is "Dozens, but only two of them were my own".

Being abroad in sunnier climates made it easy for the women (and Men) to fall in love with the Reps. They see a confident, popular, constantly happy, usually Hunky and Suntanned guy or girl (Myself being the exception), living la vida loca, skiing, windsurfing and partying non-stop all the time. Admired by other Guys, desired by other women which made them seem all the more unobtainable and touched that competitive streak and wanting within them. We were the prize target, up there in front of them always smiling and full of energy.

To be fair we were a breed apart, with incredible stamina, both physical and mental strength in abundance, entertainers, confidants, diplomats, social organisers, leaders not followers. Always last to bed and first up and leading from the front. If it needed done we were there. This was our home town and we could show you where to have a good time. There was sometimes jealousy and competition amongst the Billys about who was going to bed the rep but it was usually blown over by next morning. I did get one girl complaining to Alan about my attitude and behaviour, which had surprised me. On deeper investigation from Alan's interrogation of me he asked "Did you shag her?" "No I did not shag her" I exclaimed somewhat hurt. "Did you shag her friend?"

to which wild accusation I was astounded. "Well....erm yes I did". Alan's greater experience of this holiday game told him that this was the problem. She had wanted to shag me and her friend had gazumped her therefore pissing her off somewhat. I was a bit surprised at that, because she only had to have asked me and I would have shagged her too.

So on the surface we Reps were golden Adonis's gliding elegantly along the water's surface like graceful swans, but in reality we were furiously pedalling underwater trying to stay afloat. We seemed trustworthy and in control, whilst behind the scenes however, we were a bunch of misfits running around sorting rooming lists, coach transfers, flights for people who wanted to curtail their holiday and fly home early because they were missing someone or had an emergency back home.

We had a few heart-breaking difficult calls to say a relative had died or been involved in an accident and had to revert from crazy fun maker to Mr Sensible and show compassion and offer support as required.

I had one poor guy on his first ever holiday abroad on his own who I had to escort to a telephone box, two days into his holiday and get him to phone his Parents when I had already been informed that his younger brother of only sixteen years of age had just died in a motorbike accident. I had to go from party animal to embracing this poor guy as he crumbled tearfully into my arms. Then escort him to the airport to get on the first available flight back to his grieving family.

We had also on more than one occasion the need to give CPR

and mouth to mouth resuscitation to guests who had collapsed whether Alcohol or water-submergent related.

I myself had a late night trip in an ambulance at high speed, with one loveable drunk Billy who had fallen thirty five feet from his balcony. The stupid idiot had leaned over the balcony to spray shaving foam at myself and some other holiday makers having a nightcap at the tables in front of the hotel. When we moved our chairs backwards beneath his reach, the silly twat misjudged his ability to lean over the balcony and I heard a loud scream and looked upwards as his body came hurtling down and landed on a car parked on the road in front of us outside the reception.

I sobered up immediately as the Adrenaline rushed through my veins and I ran over to check he was still alive. I organised an ambulance and we slowly peeled him off the car bonnet, which now had his body imprinted just like you would see on a "Wile E coyote and roadrunner" or "Tom and Jerry" cartoon show. Talk about lucky? If he had landed two foot to the right, he would have gone through the windscreen at great speed and probably severed some major arteries. If he had went two foot to the left he would have hit the concrete of the pavement and died.

Meanwhile his mates watching drunkenly from the same balcony were shouting that he was alright and just bring him back up for a beer.

One mad rush to hospital, then a few hours later he was signed out with just very bad bruising. Luckily as he was so pissed he was relaxed and without tension and as he fell the soft metal of the car had broken his fall like a stuntman falling on cardboard boxes.

The next day I put a sign on the notice board to remind the guests "If leaving the Hotel, please use the stairs". It didn't end there though. I had an inspirational quote pinned on my bedroom door on the advice of Alan the boss, it simply said P.M.A which stood for positive, mental, attitude. No matter what shit I was going through or how hungover or pissed off I was, it was all left behind in the sanctuary of my bedroom as I opened the door, took a deep breath, put on a smile and entered my stage to perform for another day.

The morning after the balcony incident or in reality three hours after getting back from the hospital, as I opened my door smiling I was met by a welcoming committee of the stuntman's friends. They stood in a group of five, looking at me very sheepishly as they patiently waited for me to emerge.

"Hi Mac, we need a word. We just found out who the car belongs to, that our mate landed on!"

Fuck. I had forgotten all about the car. It turned out that even though the hotel was exclusive contractually for our young people's group, the night shift manager would sign in the odd passing stranger for a few nights for cash in hand, if we had any spare rooms. (I am sure Dodgy Stan was involved in the deal somewhere too). Anyway, some passing Italian tourists had been booked in overnight and were blissfully unaware of the drama that had taken place as they slumbered, and were now sitting in the dining room having their continental breakfast.

"The guy is Italian Mac and doesn't speak any English. We don't speak any Italian… but you do. You are going to have to explain to him what happened".

Less than a minute later I was pleasantly introducing myself to the most Italian looking Italians I had ever seen. He was a chubby faced smiling dark skinned Super Mario look alike, with the curly dark hair and an incredibly thick bushy moustache. His wife was an attractive plump Italian mamma also with dark curly hair and a slightly less thick moustache. He was very excited that I could speak in Italian to him and was asking me the questions you would of a new acquaintance you were trying to befriend. I thought to myself, how I tell this really nice friendly guy that his car has just been trashed? I had a lightbulb above the head moment as I recalled most Italians are deeply religious and quickly formulated a plan in my mind.

I started with…"I just wanted to thank you and your wife and God for saving my friends life."

I nodded to the group of mates standing very conspicuously around two foot behind my shoulder.

"If God hadn't brought you to this hotel and made you park your car where you did, my friend would probably be dead by now." He raised one incredibly bushy eyebrow as I continued rambling.

"My friend was falling tragically to his death but by some miracle your car managed to break his fall and save his life."

He smiled and obviously appreciated his involvement in this miracle. Saying how amazingly lucky we all were.

"There is a little bit of a dent in your car however, do you want to come and take a look at it?"

He left his breakfast and walked alongside me through the hotel, still trying to be my pal and asking me where I had stayed in Italy and how long had I been there. As we turned outside past the reception desk he spotted his beloved little Italian Fiat car looking like it had been smacked by the world's largest sledge hammer, he turned even more stereotypical Italian as he sunk to his knees pulling at his hair, screaming "Mama Mia" followed by every Italian swearword I knew and plenty more that I didn't. We then began a verbal tennis match with the crowd of lads, still two foot behind my shoulder.

Italy v England round one, with a Jock translating.

"Who is gonna pay for dis a damage?" - "He wants to know who is paying for this lads."

"Tell him to go through his insurance company". Good Idea. "The boys were wondering if maybe your insurance company would cover the costs."

"How can I a tell them a man fall outda da sky and land a onna my car?" Fair Point.-

"He says how can he tell them a man dropped on it from out of the sky?"

"Tell him to fuck off." -"The lads say they will gladly pay for the damage and would like to apologise." "I no know how a mucha they wanna charge me to repair."-

"Give him some cash lads" "Tell him to fuck off." -"The boys say that don't have any holiday money left but if you send them

102

the bill, they will gladly settle it."

I turned to the lads. "Give me an address where he can send the bill."

The lads scribbled a name and address on some notepaper although I am sure that Mr N. Oddy, of 23 Toytown, London, England, probably never responded.

I am sure that somewhere in East London to this day, there is a Mafia Hit-Man with a car bonnet pressing it against passing cockneys like a lethal Prince Charming trying to fit on a concrete overcoat instead of a glass slipper.

I think I had more problems translating the cockerny rhyming slang than the Italian language. "Next time me old china, use the fucking apples and pears."

Sweaty sock indeed!

In between being an agony Aunt and splashing on my Aramis and Paco Rabanne or even Kouros after shave and furthering my studies as a very keen trainee gynaecologist, I was often interrupted mid flow when either trying to pull someone or in the actual act itself, by my hoodlums causing some chaos somewhere around the resort.

I already mentioned my airport arrival speech for any of the newcomers that looked like trouble and one of these groups from Birmingham had recently arrived.

At the airport they looked like they were on a mission to get into a scrap as soon as they landed and were scowling at airport staff and fellow passengers alike. There was about eight in the group and they ranged in height and shape but each boasted fascial scars that told you to keep well out of their way. They took their place in the back seats of the transfer coach. I tried to engage them in friendly conversation asking which part of Birmingham they were from and which teams they supported, but was met by grunts and more scowls. I decided we weren't going to be bosom buddies and so I gave them the speech.

"Lads you obviously don't want to join in with my banter and it is obvious you are looking for trouble, so let me explain how this is going to work. I am your lifeline, your get out of Jail card. Without me you are helpless so do not try to alienate me before we have even checked you in. you are welcome to join in with all our activities but don't cause any trouble around my hotel or I will have you deported. If you want to cause trouble then do it at the other end of the resort and we will get along fine."

I don't know if they took that as an instruction because that is exactly what they did. Every night I was getting reports of them fighting or smashing up some bars at the other end of town but luckily no one ever linked them to us. A couple of them even came on a few of the trips and were as good as gold with their behaviour.

In most foreign hotels you are checked out of the rooms by late morning and due to the nature of getting the cheaper flights with our group, the flight home was probably much, much later in the evening or night. This was when most people usually did their last minute shopping for presents and taking those last minute tourist photographs. Yobbos on the other hand tend to spend these last few hours getting absolutely wasted on whatever drinks their last few pesetas can buy.

I was trying to have a few hours of afternoon delight with a new arrival and was oblivious to what was happening outwith my bedroom walls. Danny banged on my door in a rather unusually frantic manner shouting at the top of his voice. It had all kicked off big style in the bar next to the hotel and I could hear the sirens as the ambulance and police arrived to do their thing. The bored Brummies had decided that, as there was no one else around to cause trouble with, they would just fight amongst themselves. The biggest one of the group who had a gouge out of the area under his eye decide to accuse his mate of sleeping with his woman, which totally bemused the guy he was accusing and he stared back at him incredulously. Before he had a chance to protest his innocence, the accuser smacked him across the head with a Bar stool and the rest of them piled in after picking the team they were fighting for. It then descended into an old western movie style bar brawl with glasses chairs and punches being thrown everywhere. The bar owner had phoned the emergency services and they filled their vans with the appropriate bodies, some off to hospital and some off to the police station.

So now I had a bus arriving in around one and a half hours to take them to the Airport and only two of the Brummies still standing in the hotel. Danny and I had some frantic rushing around trying to get the police to release their "Collars" and they would not agree until the one who was currently residing in hospital due to his concussion, appeared at the Police station to confirm he was not pressing charges. We therefore had to convince the hospital to release him into our care and then try to keep him standing upright while he tried to convince the police that his assailant and his assistants were still his best mates. He was totally spaced out and wanting to hug anyone who came near him and embraced his psychopathic mate as they brought him from the cells to the front desk.

"He is my best pal he is" he muttered as the Nutcase scowled back at him.

Then we shifted them onto the transfer bus and let the airline staff take over from there.

The hospital and police station were regular haunts of mine as I tried to keep my hoodlums and nutcases under control. I had one spell of daily visits to the hospital for various reasons over one busy month.

One of my female Billys was out for a nice quiet meal and had decided to try some "crêpes flambé" where alcohol is poured over the food and it is briefly set alight. It usually looked quite spectacular and she decided to lean in closer in order for her friend to take a photograph of the occasion. The waiter obviously trying to be flash and show off to the pretty girls started applying more and more alcohol from his plastic squirting receptacle to make the flame more impressive. Unfortunately as the flame grew higher, he too edged closer until all of a sudden the plastic container exploded covering my Billy in alcohol and flames. Luckily a very switched on customer at a nearby table ran over and threw a jug of water over the flaming Billy and then patted out the flames with a table cover. We had an ambulance rush her off to hospital and the police quickly arrest the waiter before he scarpered. It may seem harsh as it was obviously accidental, but there were going to be questions about incompetence and also the possibility of very expensive health care.

As it turned out we did have to fly an air ambulance over to collect the Billy and fly her directly to Newcastle's special burns unit where she eventually received skin grafts. In the meantime she spent a few days at the local hospital where everyone in the hotel, it seemed wanted to visit her.

I had been to see her a few times and she was in good spirits in spite of her obvious pain and lay in a bed covered by a wire cage to keep contact off her black and charred skin which in turn was covered by paper sheets. She lay naked under the paper covered cage and bits of her skin looked as though they were flaking off, unable to bend or move her arms, you couldn't help but feel sorry for the poor girl. I placed a chair by her bedside and chatted for a while keeping her spirits up as more and more guests arrived to visit and as they placed their chairs at her bedside too, I was gradually moving my chair further and further up towards her headboard. Eventually I realised my head was alongside hers giving me an unobstructed Ariel view of her slim naked body as I glanced down. I had seen many naked female bodies so I wasn't really fazed by the view, but what did distract me uncomfortably was that there was a piece of orange fluff on her Muff and my eyes kept being drawn towards it even as I tried to look at the other visitors who were in deep conversation and unaware at my predicament. Eventually it became too much and I leaned forward and apologised to her as I reached down to her fluff covered lady parts and rummaged through her pubic hair to remove the offending article.

As everyone else looked back at me somewhat taken aback, my poor Billy looked me in the eye and said "Thanks Mac, that has been getting on my nerves for the last two days."

Most ironic of all was that the girl was called Suzanne and it took a lot of control not to mention the "Crêped Suzanne" incident without sniggering like a schoolboy.

Chapter Ten

Family Matters

My Parents had slowly thawed to the idea of my new life of debauchery abroad and were flying out to visit. I sensibly took the precaution of booking them an apartment a few miles away from our hotel. My mum and dad were a bit of a contradiction in the fact that they had very strong morals and principals in what should be acceptable behaviour but at the same time they were a pair of party animals and terrific fun to be around. They were a typical wee Glasgow man and wife who always sounded as though they were constantly arguing and having a fight with each other, but woe betide anyone else who tried to have a go at them.

They would be arriving for a week's visit and were bringing my young thirteen year old brother Brendan with them. My older sister had decided not to come along which to be truthful suited me fine. I have rarely ever seen eye to eye with my sister, but I still speak to her just in case I need a compatible donor kidney sometime in the future. I didn't foresee any immediate problems ahead as they would do their own thing during the day and then come out on a few of the evening excursions over the following week.

It was great to see them and I had managed to clear the evidence from my hotel room before my Mother had a nosey around. It went ok at the start as she complimented the size of the room and noticed I had my own shower and toilet. The bed was made and looked inviting, at least it was till my wee brother decided to launch himself onto it, pulling up the sheets that overhung the sides in the process, exposing a pair of discarded women's knickers underneath the bed. I had to quickly explain that my cleaner had probably dropped them off the top of her pile of ironing accidentally when she was delivering my clothes. I got a filthy disapproving look from my Mother but I think I got away with it.

The usual plan for an evening excursion was to meet the Billys in the bar area early evening, then climb on board the bonkers bus to the trip. We would spend the night entertaining them, get them drunk and happy, then have a sing song on the bus trip back home again. It was foolproof.

I told my mum and dad the meeting time at my hotel and arranged to meet them in the bar area. I bounced into the bar twenty minutes before the rendezvous time only to find all of my Billys pissed out of their heads with some of them hardly able to stand up. It turns out mum and dad had arrived early and decided to start the party before I got there. It was a disaster, people were throwing up on the coach or falling asleep before we had even started the trip. My parents many years of drinking experience had made their alcohol tolerance system almost immune to its effects and instead of making my usual informative introduction to the trip through the bus microphone, I looked up the bus to find only my mum, dad and wee brother smiling attentively back at me, while my Billys lay scattered comatose in the aisle.

I made sure my dad was the butt of every joke on every occasion. We sent him down the biggest waterslide flume with the largest drop at the Waterslide Park and watched the horror on his face as he reached the end of the slide and suddenly realised the distance he was about to fall. We dressed him as a woman for our Miss World night with full make up and panty hose which he would have hated and picked him for all the little games we did. We had a few party tricks that we usually played in the bars and one of these involved getting three or four Billys and my dad at one end of the room then placing a glass tumbler on a chair around 15 feet away. We would take out a coin and get the Billy to grip it between the cheeks of their backside and walk to the chair then reverse their bum and attempt to drop the coin into the glass tumbler.

We made a big show of holding the coin in the air and instructing the Billy to clench their butt cheeks to take hold of the coin. The crowd would cheer wildly as they slowly edged their footsteps towards the waiting glass tumbler.

Some of them would get quite near and you would hear the coin bounce off the rim of the glass as success narrowly escaped them.

My dad had a very technical thought process and decided that the slower he walked and the shorter his steps were, the chances he would drop the coin would lessen. I pushed the coin deep into the cleft of his buttocks and watched as he painstakingly slowly edged forward like a snail on treacle, with the watching crowd screaming their encouragement by cheering and whooping every step he took. As he reached the chair he slowly turned and reversed his bum over the glass, then relaxed his sphincter to release the coin, but nothing happened. He stamped his foot a little to release the coin that was obviously stuck in the material of his shorts, but still nothing. It was at this point I would draw his attention to the coin I held aloft 15 feet away and apologised that I had forgot to let the coin go. I was met with a barrage of abuse from my Father as he ironically questioned my parentage.

Young Brendan was in his element to be involved in this "grown up" world and enjoyed his daily mid-morning walk along the beach tripping over sunbathing tourists and standing on heads and hands as he tried to stroll up and down the sands nonchalantly, drinking in the many naked bosoms on show all around him. His head moved from side to side like car windscreen wipers on top speed as he feasted his eyes on all the flesh scattered around the beach. He was well liked by our group and I would routinely find him buried in the sand up to his neck when he had eventually became too much of a pain in the arse.

My young brother hero worshipped me and no wonder, as I introduced him to his rite of passage way before his due time.

The poor lad found his sexual awakening and was transforming from a naïve thirteen year old into a man over one eventful long week in Spain. He looked older than his thirteen years to be fair, at first glance you would assume he was around seventeen. He was a good looking boy and was fortunate enough to have inherited some of his big brothers charm and humour. Some of the girls found him adorable and cute, while some wanted to mother and nurse him, I think he was actually breastfed on a couple of occasions.

I was a responsible adult and quite capable of keeping an eye on him when he suggested mum and dad left him in my care after the excursions as they headed back to their rented apartment. I was usually very reliable and sensible and I was aware of my surrogate parental duties... at least I was, till I got drunk and horny and would wander off with my newest conquest for another night of horizontal pleasure, forgetting everything as my one eyed snake started to stir.

I would awake in the morning in a panic thinking "where the Fuck did I leave my Wee Brother?" and spend the next hour trying to retrace my movements from the previous night, frantically knocking on the doors of the girl guests I had briefly seen him talking with. Eventually I would find him in the bedroom of a couple of girls in a twin room, snuggled up beside one of them, grinning at me like a Cheshire cat who just had the proverbial cream. "Don't you dare tell Mum" he was reminded daily as I dropped him back at the rented apartment in time for his cornflakes, before rushing off immediately to avoid the inevitable interrogation of where we had been.

Brendan earned God like status when he returned to school and the teacher asked the kids to stand up and report about how they spent their holidays. There was the usual kid in short pants regaling how they had went to Butlins with their cousins and played table tennis and swam daily, or the kids explaining "We went to Blackpool Miss and saw the roller coasters at the pleasure beach".

The bold Brendan stood up and said "Do you want to see some holiday snaps?" and threw a pile of incriminating Polaroid's on the desks in front of him, like a Poker shark revealing four aces. In every picture there were numerous bare tits on show, with a smiling Brendan peering out from somewhere in the photo, usually framed by a pair of 38DD's.

I fully accept culpability for ruining Brendan's expectations of a normal life from that moment on and apologise whole-heartedly.

My mum and dads memory of the trip was slightly soured by one wee incident at Stan and Kaz's Hotel. We didn't have a pool at my hotel and I therefore arranged for my folks to use the pool at our sister hotel which was nearby. One evening after a long day of sunbathing as they packed their things and tried to find their way out of the unfamiliar building, they took a wrong turn down some steps and ended up going slowly downwards into the hotel basement where the pool house machinery and junk was kept. On seeing all the dusty wine bottles, junk and storage rooms with their locked doors, my dad realised their mistake and looked around for the best exit. He spotted an old fashioned "two man" lift straight ahead of them which was sometimes used to carry the bar stock upstairs or remove an old mattress back downstairs to the basement. It was dusty and covered with cobwebs, with a little square window in the middle of the one metal door. They entered the lift with all their belongings and pressed the button to take them back up to the reception area, then watched horrified as the lift moved about an inch and shuddered to a halt. Dad tried to open the door again but it was fastened shut as the extra inch of movement now prevented the door opening. Dad glanced out the little square window and it suddenly dawned on him that they could be trapped in there for a very long time as there was no sign of any passing human traffic, no emergency button and no reason for anyone to actually go down into the pits of the cellar. He tried to calm his hyper irate moaning wife as he explained they had one half bottle of water, some suntan lotion, towels and a Mills and Boon book to survive on for god knows how long.

Surely someone would eventually have to come past.

Their salvation came almost ninety minutes later in the shape of "Carlos" the dumb waiter who had been sent into the basement for a crate of mineral waters. Dad was gratefully relieved to see movement outside the little window and even more ecstatic to see Carlos walk towards the lift door. Carlos tried to pull the door open, but it would not budge. He tried once again more forcefully but it was stuck fast. My dad tapped on the window to alert Carlos, who gave a vacant stare straight back into his eyes. "It's broken pal!" said my Dad in his thick Glasgow accent.

"Ees ok "said Carlos "I use the stairs" and with that, he turned away with his crate of mineral waters in his arms and headed up the stairs out of the basement, as my parents stared open mouthed in horror at the unbelievably thick Spaniard.

"Does he think were standing in here to tell him the fucking lift is broken?" yelped my dad to my mum as they started bickering for the next ninety minutes. Finally one of the cleaners heard their screams and the odd job man arrived with the emergency door key. I had to hide Carlos from my Dad for the next three days as he promised to deliver the famous "Glasgow Kiss" as a parting gift when he found him. To this day my dad is still suspicious of anyone Spanish and my mum won't use any lift at all.

We had all sorts of people arrive at our hotels from the usual party animal yobbos to the shyer types on the peripheral of the activities. Once we had a young couple who were together but only really in spirit.

Edward and Pamela breezed through our doors one day within a batch of new arrivals and you could sense a square peg being placed in a round hole. They were on holiday with another couple of friends, James and Kate who were a bit more like our normal holidaying type.

Edward was a big physical specimen, around six foot three tall and had shoulders as wide as a wardrobe and obviously looked after himself. He had American style Donny Osmond teeth which appeared a bit too big for his mouth and he was a perfect gentleman, treating Pamela like a porcelain doll.

He cringed visibly whenever anyone swore within earshot and you could sense how uncomfortable he was with our infamous party games. I got the impression that Pamela had talked him into the holiday in an effort to loosen him up and get her some much needed fun.

Pamela was pretty and I could sense a caged tiger within her who was straining to be let off the leash. Kate and James were fun but Edward just didn't seem to fit in anywhere.

The weirdest thing about the foursome was the sleeping arrangements, the girls shared a twin room while the two lads shared a separate twin room.

It turned out that Edward was a god fearing man and a bit of a bible thumper. He did not believe in sex outside of marriage and having Pamela in a different room would remove the temptation of forbidden flesh. Edward would be found most nights on his knees at the side of the bed with his head bowed and my reps intuition told me that given half a chance Pamela would also be on her knees at the side of a bed.

She was a bit flirty whenever she managed to escape the overpowering presence of Edward for a few minutes and was enjoying the attention of strange men looking at her with admiring glances, massaging her ego in a manner that it craved.

Most of the Billys would realise she was off limits and when they saw the physique of big Edward constantly at her shoulder, that was enough to extinguish any lingering interest.

You can't however leave a blood trail in the water where

sharks are present and more than one rep could taste the potential ripe pickings from across the room.

Wee Brian won the race to win her heart and all the associated parts that came with it. Later that evening during the party Brian manage to slip unnoticed into the bedroom with Pamela and Kate. Kate was pretty cool about things and just turned her gaze as Brian battered away like a little piston engine on Pamela, when all of a sudden there was a knock at the bedroom door and it slowly began to open, with Edward telling the girls to make sure they were decent as he was coming in to say goodnight to Pamela. Brian hid trembling under the covers and slid down to make sure his head was not visible over the top of the blankets.

He felt the draught at his feet which had unfortunately protruded from the end of the bed, but luckily the room was in darkness so he was not too visible.

Big Edward leaned over the bed and put one hand either side of Pamela's shoulders as he leaned in to kiss her and Brian felt the heat from his big hand as it landed an inch from his nose on the mattress.

Edward walked back to the door and said his goodnights to the girls' one at a time. Like the Walton's used to do at the end of the TV show. Wee Brian held his breath.

"Goodnight and god bless you Kate", "Goodnight Edward" she responded.

"Goodnight and God bless Pamela" "Goodnight Edward" she replied.

Edward opened the door and gave one last "May God keep you all safe in your sleep tonight" and for some idiotic reason that we still can't figure out, Brian blurted out "Goodnight Edward".

I was sitting outside the hotel having a few beers with some Billys as a bollock naked Brian came sprinting past and almost flew up the main street heading back to his apartment block, followed a few seconds later by a big red faced, screaming Edward, who had obviously recently picked up a few of the swear words that used to offend him.

Chapter Eleven

Special People

As time passes by whilst repping, you become more mercenary towards the Billys and from being sorry for the "Loner" type of person, you suddenly realise that the runt of the litter was usually the best candidate to take the brunt of all the jokes.

At the welcome meetings which was usually your first glimpse of the new arrivals, you would spot the "Geeks" in the corner, the ones who had at no point in their life ever had a girlfriend or even a friend, in some cases even their parents had accepted they were a closet case. Some people were special and some were "special" people. We had all sorts of personalities and types on our holidays from the psychotic steroid fuelled weightlifters who wanted to drop me off the balcony to the overly friendly ladies and poor unfortunate "Billy no mates" who were a sandwich short of a picnic.

Sam was an exceptional specimen, he looked like a cross between a child molester and Worzel Gummidge the scarecrow, with his unkempt hair, pock marked complexion and a dried up snot channel beneath his nose, further enhanced by specks of blood all over his chin as he never seemed to shave properly. His sixties fashion sense included his flared trousers and tank tops and to top the look off he had bits missing, namely some teeth, three middle fingers and a large portion of his peanut sized brain. I asked Sam out of curiosity what had happened to his middle three fingers as the poor lad only had his thumb and pinkie finger on his left hand. "Oh I used to be a butcher" was his valid explanation. I bet they don't sell many sausages in that shop anymore, I thought.

Sam unsurprisingly was a "Single share" who arrived on his own and was given a shared room with someone else. He was a loveable, harmless guy when you got to know him, but out-with this holiday I doubt people would waste that time finding out. He would spot a group of people and latch onto them and whatever you could do, Sam could do…only better. Small groups of people sunbathing and chatting on the roof would have Sam bursting in "I've done that" whether it be Ballroom dancing at Blackpool pier or parachuting into the Borneo Jungle Sam had medals for it. We got to the stage that when we knew he was earwigging we would make up a scenario.

"Yeah I remember when I went shark fishing without a line and had to hold the bait over the side of the boat."

Sam's cue to come over "I've done that once at Brighton beach."

He was Mr Charisma and could empty a room in a few minutes of arriving, but with some small assistance from Danny and me, amongst my Billys he was an adopted Idol for his whole fortnight stay.

Any volunteers for Beach party games, Sam was up first, any karaoke requests on stage, hand Sam the Microphone. We even persuaded him to stitch up a famous magician in a very exclusive nightclub. Myself and Danny had seen the show a dozen times and knew the routine so we made sure our group was ready at the right time. The suave man of mystery asked for a volunteer to do the famous "Guillotine" trick where he first cut through a carrot with one sharp drop of the guillotine, our crowd went crazy shouting for Sam to do the trick and the magician obviously keen to please the crowd picked Sam to come up on stage. He placed the finger on Sam's right hand under the sharp blade and slammed it dramatically down as he turned to milk the applause from the crowd, only to be met by screams, gasps and fainting ladies as Sam held up his left hand missing the three fingers, covered in tomato sauce, with a pained expression on his face. Needless to say when the Magician regained his normal facial colour, he made us disappear out of the club on our arses.

We invented our own "Spanish Wave" adapted so that Sam could join in. the wave involved extending your thumb and pinkie out and curling in the three middle fingers into your palms making a horns shape on both hands, then waving your arms above your head. We would be in a club and the shout would sound "Give us a Spanish wave" and everyone from the hotel group would wave their hands in the air, including Sam who would receive the biggest cheers for joining in.

The guys from my hotel loved it and all day and night you would hear someone shouting randomly "Give us a wave" followed by excited cheers as everyone obliged. We had a nice group of girls staying at the hotel the same week as Sam and one of the girls had big rounded frames on her glasses as was the fashion in those days. We had christened her Deirdre as the glasses were similar to the ones worn by the Coronation street pin up.

Deirdre couldn't swim and was a bit scared to venture into the sea with her friends and sat on the beach beside me chatting. The sea was quite calm and there was quite a distance before the water level became too deep to stand in, so I persuaded Deirdre to walk into the water holding my arm until it reached just above her waist and she nervously edged deeper and deeper until the water supported her just above the waist. The gentle motion of the sea would push her slightly to and fro and she enjoyed this new sensation so much that she became confident enough to be left on her own as I reclaimed my spot in the sand. Things were going fine for a while and Deirdre was smiling away as she faced back to her friends and the rest of us on the beach, but suddenly in the distance I spotted a motor boat in full flight zooming across the horizon behind her with a water-skier in tow. There was no danger from the boat or skier but the wake behind the boat had created a massive, almost tidal wave that was quickly advancing to the poor unsuspecting smiling Deirdre. I stood up gesturing for her to look over her shoulder and shouted "Wave, Wave" pointing at the advancing sea. Deirdre smiled back at me and put her hands in the air with the horns sign waving frantically back at me as the wave twatted her, knocking her off her feet and forcing her face into the sand beneath her. She eventually stood up looking like the proverbial drowned rat, spluttering and coughing up sea water minus her "Deirdre specs" which were never to be found again.

Sam always looked unkempt with the messy hair and dried blood on his face and if he shuffled over to strangers in a Disco, they would quickly give him a wide berth, which was the polar opposite of being a rep because people would surround you and your magic badge. I wondered if maybe the missing fingers made it difficult to shave properly. I had an idea that for one night only I would transfer Sam's meagre existence into a life he could only dream of, he was about to be Willy Wonka and I was about to give him the golden ticket.

7.30pm in the bar tonight
witness Sam's transformation
as tonight he becomes our Rep

I placed a poster on the notice board my thought process was that I could shave him and as there were normally a few hairdressers on holiday with us, one of the girls could wash and blow dry his hair. We could borrow some trendy clothes from someone and I was going to place the sacred Magic badge on his chest temporarily. It would also give me the luxury of transforming myself into a beer soaked British holiday yobbo and blend in with the normal Billys. The joke would be on everyone else as we all knew Sam was a bit of a knob, but none of the unsuspecting tourists who met him that night would know that.

7.30 pm duly arrived and in the centre of our packed out hotel bar area I had placed a chair in the middle of the floor, whilst we played a fanfare to announce Sam's arrival as the star guest. He confidently breezed into the room already looking immaculate in the borrowed leather trousers and pristine white cotton shirt with his hair coiffured to perfection. All I had to do now was wipe the snot channel from his nose, shave him properly and adorn him with the coveted prized Reps badge. I instructed him to quickly go and get his shaving gear and in a few minutes he was back with a mug of hot water and a disposable Bic razor. I took them from him and placed them on a table to the side and asked him

"Where is your shaving foam?"

He replied "Shaving foam? I don't use shaving foam"

The stupid twat had been slicing his face open every day for years with no barrier between his skin and the blade and I thought it was because he couldn't grip the blade.

"Do you shave like that every morning Sam?" I asked him.

"Oh no, I don't shave in the mornings, I do it when we get back from the Discotheque to save me time in the mornings"

Rough shaving in the dark while pissed with missing fingers, what could possibly go wrong, and I was about to hand this clown my prized possession.

We had a great night out with Sam being surrounded by everyone in the discos and bars saying

"it must be great being on holiday all the time? And how long have you been a Rep" then Sam replying with a straight face

"Not that long actually".

I was meanwhile getting pissed with my shorts, vest and union jack hat shouting "ere we go, ere we go" at every opportunity whilst throwing popcorn at everyone and generally being a complete wanker, which was fine until I realised without the badge I was going to have to pay for my drinks and risked being barred from the pubs for being an arsehole.

I managed to get the badge back before Sam decided to take people on his own pub crawl like the pied piper. It was a lesson learned that although I had a lot of personality, it was the power of the badge that allowed us to abuse our position and not that we were supreme beings after all. I would love to have seen the look on some poor young lady that wakened beside Sam the next day thinking she had bedded one of the Reps.

Chapter Twelve

Absolutely Mental

The Doctors surgery was a regular haunt of mine for many reasons and luckily enough our local Doctor also owned the hotel that Kaz and Stan looked after, along with his lovely wife who manned the front reception desk. They were a very jovial fun couple and had a son, who was a bit "special". Fernando was almost twenty but had a mental age of around ten and he was resident in a school that took care of his needs throughout the week, Monday to Thursday, but he spent the weekends with us at the hotel.

Fernando would casually lurk around the pool area staring at the bare boobs on show and chatting to the guests who adopted him as our sort of own little hotel mascot. He spoke excellent English and was fascinated by the many different accents we had amongst us, he was also a very good mimic and could usually pick up the regional twang in a "Rain Man" sort of way. This caused great amusement around the pool when he repeated phrases he had picked up in previous conversations. Watching this big powerful, handsome dark tanned guy, speaking to groups of people and switching between accents from Geordie brogue to Cockney rhyming slang within a few sentences was incredible and he was so personable, you would instantly forget his mental thought process was that of a young child. You would occasionally spot him playing with a toy and remember he was just a kid, trapped in a man's body. It was also fun watching him interacting with the new arrivals when they encountered him for the first time as they gazed back at him in disbelief.

One of Fernando's favourite sounds was the beautiful lilt of an Irish accent, like the ones he first heard at the start of the season when he met a crowd of lovely Irish nurses who were celebrating their graduation. The girls always made a fuss of him and delighted in corrupting his inquisitive mind, with tales of their mystical land full of Leprechauns and pots of gold under every rainbow. He was fascinated by it all and when the girls returned to Ireland they sent him a little gift package with cartoon books of leprechauns and a little stuffed ginger bearded cuddly leprechaun which immediately became Fernando's favourite toy. For the next few months Fernando walked about cuddling his new friend, speaking to him in an Southern Irish accent and greeting the guests with a "how about ye?" and "the craic is mighty so." He was a star was our Fernando.

I was visiting his Dad Juan the Doctor two or three times a week, with various Billys and their ailments, mostly Sunstroke or occasionally for stitches in their heads when they fell of Mopeds or dived into the empty pool when drunk. I had a few sunburnt Billys and one of my favourite tricks was to draw noughts and crosses on them or write obscene words with a roll on sunblock I carried with me, knowing it wouldn't show till later in the day. Dr Juan would just stare at me with a knowing look of what had happened, shaking his head as he applied the cream.

He was very patient with our group and our regular disasters, even when we had to call him out during the night to one of our other hotels. One of our crowd "Marty" had unfortunately entered into a drinking contest with some American GIs who were on "Vacation" at our resort and had accepted a challenge from "Bacardi Bob" over who could consume the most Bacardi. The contest went on all night and as his friends turned up for breakfast in the morning they found Marty and Bacardi Bob still sitting across the table facing each other as they ate their morning cornflakes, but soaked in Bacardi instead of Milk. They had been up all night matching each other drink for drink and were almost paralytic.

A few hours later they called it a creditable draw and Marty was assisted back up the stairs to his bed. Later that night I was interrupted in my nightly physical manoeuvres by someone banging on my door and it turned out to be Marty's friends who desperately needed to call a Doctor due to the worrying state of Marty's condition. I told them there would be a call out charge for an emergency Doctor and then phoned the number at Dr Juan's clinic. So around 3.30am poor old Dr Juan left his comfortable bed to drag himself to my hotel and examine yet another drunken British tourist. The diagnosis was obviously alcoholic poisoning and Dr Juan got his syringe ready to administer the injection into Marty's Buttocks, which cause great amusement amongst Marty's friends as they all pushed past to grab their Polaroid cameras to capture Marty's moment of discomfort.

Marty was to be confined to bed rest the next day in a darkened room and instructed to only drink water. We popped in to see him a few times the next day as he sweated out the worst hangover ever. Later that night I was once again interrupted in my nightly physical activities with Marty's friends again banging on my door, panicking as he had another relapse and was in as bad as state as he had been the previous night. Again they would need an emergency Doctor and again they would have to pay another call out charge. Yet again I phoned the emergency number at Dr Juan's clinic and a locum Doctor was dispatched to examine Marty in his hour of need. The Doctor pressed his stomach and did various tests as I stood at the side translating between the Doctor and a very uncomfortable irate Marty who kept telling me to tell the Doctor "Its alcoholic poisoning, tell him its alcoholic poisoning". The Doctor put away his stethoscope and gave me the diagnosis. I found great pleasure in relaying the news to Marty and his concerned mates that the diagnosis was in fact "Water poisoning". The silly twat had been drinking fizzy water all day instead of sipping still water to rehydrate him and he had too many bubbles in his bloodstream and gas in his bloated belly. The ignominy of it all, Marty was the only Billy in the world to ever suffer the heartbreak of missing two days holiday fun because of drinking water as he was yet again confined to bed for the following day. Cue another syringe in the arse as the cameras flashed once again.

One health problem I did not expect to encounter during my seasons in the sun was mental health. Without any training or experience I don't think anyone could spot mental illness, let alone know how to handle it and we were not anywhere near ready for it. "Greg" had arrived with a crowd of friends from Swindon and was the livewire of the group. He was loud and funny and very hyperactive and in one or two passing conversations with him, I began to wonder if he was "a few clowns short of a circus". I called him Greg the Bungalow as he definitely had nothing upstairs. His big googly eyes just bulged out as he got more and more excitable with every sentence. One day at random he faced up to me in front of his mates, taking up a martial arts type stance and challenging me to a fight. I imagine I was supposed to back down or take fright, but instead I took up a "proper" Martial Arts stance and stared him square in his googly eyes and told him "you better be really good at this pal, because I've been training at this for fourteen years". I think he hoped I would be embarrassed but instead it was him backing down and scurrying away when he looked in my eyes and knew I meant business. He laughed out loud and scarpered before it got physical. What a weirdo I thought.

A few days later one of his friends confided in me that he was a bit worried about how Greg was acting recently and thought he was behaving a little more oddly than usual. He had showed his friend a holiday souvenir that he had bought and produced from his suitcase a "Rambo" style knife around twelve inches long with serrated edges. He then told his mate he was going to kill himself and then quickly added "no, I've changed my mind, I'm not going to do it."

A few mornings later as I popped my head into the hotel reception, the receptionist was grinning and told me to look in

Greg's room. The scene in the room was like a real life horror movie, there was blood splattered up and down the walls and broken glass scattered across the floor from the now shattered sliding balcony doors. "What the fuck happened, has someone walked through here with a chainsaw?" the still grinning receptionist explained how Greg "he go crazy". The story unfolded that during the night Greg had wakened his roommates by announcing he was going to kill himself again. One of his mates had replied "well fucking do it quietly then." Which brought the response from Greg and his bulging pupils "I've changed my mind… I'm going to take you with me" as he grabbed his mate by the ankle and projected both of them through the still closed glass patio doors onto the balcony. The ensuing carnage involved Police, ambulances and numerous panicking Billys and resulted in a sedated Greg and his pal being admitted into the local hospital.

When I arrived at the hospital, Greg was coming around and was in a sorry state indeed, with dried blood all over his body and weeping cuts on his face and arms. The foreign hospitals don't seem to have the same standards as our beloved NHS and the prison style bed and the grey walls surrounding him did little to lighten the atmosphere. It was the same the next day when I visited again but he still had not been cleaned up and neither had the dried blood all over the bedsheets. He seemed calm and was talking perfectly normally but could not remember a single thing about the incident that had put him in here. For a bit of a giggle I had drawn a little stick man on a sheet of folded paper as a get well soon card and pinned it on the wall beside his bed. He smiled and all was calm as I left the hospital quite content that he would be discharged and back in the bosom of our group within a few days and it would be business as usual.

Next day I arrived at an empty hospital bed with the imprint of his body still outlined in the dried blood framing the sheets and I worryingly feared the worst as I rushed to find a nurse. She explained that during the previous night Greg had gone crazy again because he thought the stick man on the wall had been sent to kill him!!! He had now been placed in a straitjacket in a padded room. We had to contact our head office back home who sent over a psychiatric nurse to escort Greg back to the UK. The nurse who arrived was the biggest guy I had ever seen, with shoulders as wide as a wardrobe and was also the calmest man with a soft soothing tone of voice that immediately calmed Greg down. He took total control of the situation and would be escorting Greg onto the airplane back home, making sure he never "kicked off" again on the journey. My job with Greg stopped the minute he left on the plane and I have no idea how the story ended for him. Hopefully he never took the Rambo knife home with him, but more worryingly he may even still be roaming free and walking amongst us today.

Danny had a similar type of problem one day when he found a Billy on the top of the hotel roof ready to jump over the edge. His reason for ending it all was that the girl he had managed to pull and had slept with the previous night had decide that this was as far as she wanted their "relationship" to go. He was distraught because he thought she was the girl of his dreams and therefore wanted to end it all. We had already nicknamed the girl in question after a fizzy drink as "seven up" as the number of flings she had already achieved before he arrived and took his turn.

Danny stood ten yards from him trying to talk him off the building like he had seen it happen in many "Cop" movies, but couldn't understand how this guy could be so upset over a "Girl". There were hundreds more to choose from in the resort and to be so upset over one individual was scrambling his brain as he tried to comprehend this fact. To be fair to Danny, anything over thirty minutes was a long term relationship as far as we were concerned, but Danny manfully tried his negotiating skills.

"Don't do it mate, she's not worth it" he shouted.

"But I love her" was the whimpering response.

Danny countered "there's lots of other girls here mate, pick another".

"But she's the one I want" the Billy tearfully explained.

Danny was now clutching at straws and had one last attempt. "come on mate you don't want to kill yourself over some piece of skirt?" "Why shouldn't I kill myself?" the Billy blubbered.

Danny's final bargaining chip was, "I don't know how to fill the paperwork if you die". We eventually had to get "Seven up" onto the roof to talk him down.

Chapter Thirteen

Three's company

We had many, many fun guests arrive at our hotel and it made our lives as social organisers a whole lot easier when you had exceptional characters and personalities to either lead the way or else have the piss ripped out of them.

We had Dave the human dustbin who was a skinny little lad who just devoured everything edible within reach. If you had leftovers on the plate he would ask "are you going to eat that?" in the hope you would say you were not. We had Sebastien the stutterer, Polly the Porn star and "Studley".

Studley was a fat, leering obnoxious greasy lout who arrived on his own and immediately started getting everyone's back up. He fancied himself as a ladies man, but had no charm or wit or looks or anything at all endearing, but he believed he was a "Stud" hence the nickname of Studley that we had christened him with.

His approach with the girls was primitive and over-direct as he just skipped straight to the point. "Do you want to come to my room and shag me?" was his usual chat-up line. He just made everyone feel very uncomfortable.

We had a duty to ensure everyone had a good holiday and would always work very hard to make this happen. We allowed him a couple of days to see if he settled down but he was becoming a pest, so Danny put his unique creativity to use and came up with a cunning plan.

Danny could charm the birds from the trees or even the birds from their underwear whenever he wanted so he got a little group of three female undercover assassins to be the Honey trap for his sting. They were sent on a mission to use their sexual charms on Studley and lure him to his bedroom. Danny's thought process was that with Studley being a fat greasy uncouth lump, he probably was not all that successful or experienced with members of the opposite sex. His plan was to get his own "Charlies Angels" team to chat up Studley with the pretence of having some sexual shenanigans with him if he fancied the challenge of taking on all three of them at once. They were supposed to entice him back to the room and use their womanly charms to strip him of his clothes and leave him in full state of arousal, then we could burst in with the Polaroid cameras and strip him of his dignity.

His room was on the ground floor and Danny had also taken the liberty of entering his room to make sure the curtains were open and that our cameraman was concealed in the wardrobe with his camera in hand. Getting in the room was easy enough because unbeknown to our guests, every single door in the building had the same lock, so any key would actually open any room.

Danny hid outside the window with a dozen or so excited Billys trying to stifle their giggles, while the trio of beauties dragged Studley into the room and threw him onto the bed. They descended on him like a plague of locusts as they frantically tore off his clothes. Studley was aroused, very aroused and was surprisingly quite impressively blessed. This did not go unnoticed amongst our female tag team and unexpectedly before we could get our cameras poised, two of the girls had disrobed and one of them had placed her mouth around Studley's impressive weapon. A moment later Danny watched in horror as one of the Trio manoeuvred herself ominously above Studley and impaled herself upon the weapon in question. There was a surge of bodies from the Billys outside the window as they pushed forward en masse trying to get a better view, including one particular lad who was desperate to get to the window.

"Let me through, let me through" he squealed

"Hang on mate wait your turn" said Danny.

"Out of my way, move it, move it" the Billy demanded.

"You'll see in a minute fella, wait your turn" said Danny.

"Shift, make way" continued the exasperated Billy.

"What's your problem geezer?" asked Danny.

"That's my Fucking wife in there!!!" replied a rather irate Billy.

I don't know if Danny kept the Polaroids but I had two horrendous days of trying to calm the situation down between the Billys and the enraged hotel management.

The Holy Grail of a threesome was a much sought after prize for any young hot bloodied male. In later life it would become difficult enough trying to keep one lady pleased, but when you're young, dumb and full of cum, it was an exciting challenge. Danny and Stan had already achieved this using their much more experienced knowledge to manipulate the situation but I had not as yet managed this rite of passage. I mentioned it one day in passing to Danny and he told me he would "Get right on it". True to his word, a few days later after a successful talent spotting mission during Airport pick up. We had our sights set on a likely target.

Two pretty girls had got off the Gatwick flight already pissed and definitely "Game". Chelsea and Becky were fun and wild but also seldom sober, this would be too easy. Using Danny's advice and coaching tips, we decided the best tactic would be to wind them up and make it a challenge or dare to enter into the threesome with me. I don't think the flowers and chocolates with dim lights and soft music would have done the trick for these two wildcats. We had planned a little disco in our hotel bar area that night and this would be the perfect conditions for snaring the prey. I was very much looking forward to it.

A few days previously a couple had arrived at the Hotel. Matt and Linda were both over six foot four inches tall and quite an impressive looking boyfriend and girlfriend. Linda was attractive but never spoke a word as Matt would hold her hand and ask questions for her, while she just smiled and looked at you. "Linda wants to know if there is a market on in Town this week." "Erm yeah, it's on a Tuesday" I replied to him, even though she was clearly within earshot, standing beside him. I smiled at her but she was probably off limits as she was actually on holiday with her Boyfriend. We sometimes had people wishing to curtail their holiday because they fell out with a partner or missed someone back home and wished to end the holiday prematurely. The first time I actually spoke to Linda I thought she was wishing to curtail.

The hotel disco was in full swing and Danny and I were winding up Chelsea and Becky a treat. I opened with "You two cockney twats are full of it!"

"What d'you fucking say, Jock?"

I continued "you're just a couple of wee lassies out of your depth here, full of chat but you couldn't handle a real man like me."

"What you fucking mean you slag?" enquired Chelsea.

"Listen girls, I may not have the biggest equipment in the world to work with here, but it's not the size of the nail, it's the size of the hammer knocking it in that's important. If I had the pair of you tonight you wouldn't be able to walk straight tomorrow."

"Fawk orf, we could handle you, you mug, easily" said Becky.

The conversation continued in this vein most of the night with Danny frequently throwing fuel on the fire. I would wander off to dance with someone and return a few drinks later as the dirty duo became more and more wasted.

"You name a time, you fucker, we'll spit you out when were finished with ya."

They proceeded to tell me in graphic what they were going to do with me, which was quite arousing if truth be told.

"Ok one o clock in my room up there"

I pointed to my room door. Amazingly the fish was truly on the hook and now I just had to slowly reel it in. I winked at Danny and danced off making gestures at my quarry and laughed at how easy it had been.

Suddenly I was grabbed forcefully by the shoulder and spun around by the Amazonian Linda, who barked at me "Dance with me!" it was definitely an order and not a request and as I smiled and rocked my shoulders from side to side with the rhythm of the music she said "Lets' go to your room".

I thought that was a weird request and maybe she had fallen out with Matt and was wanting a curtailment,

"What's wrong? Why do you want to go to my room?" I asked, raising an inquisitive eyebrow.

"I want you to fuck me" she spat.

I laughed out loud and scanned the room to see which of the

reps was trying to stitch me up.

She said "I'm serious, let's go now".

"Where's Matt?" I asked.

"Oh that boring bastard is drunk and in his bed, let's go right now. I've been waiting for a chance to fuck you since we got here." She spoke hurriedly.

Never wanting to ever let anyone down, I agreed and instructed her to leave first and I would follow in a couple of minutes. I checked again with Danny that he wasn't behind this prank and joined her outside my room, still disbelieving. I unlocked the door and entered my room and as she climbed on the bed, I checked the bathroom, wardrobe and under the bed for rogue cameramen, then glanced up to make sure all curtains were closed. It was clear. I turned to the now completely naked Linda and carried out her previous request. A few minutes later in the throes of passion, I gazed at her pretty face which was framed by her ankles around her ears, she asked me "what made you want me?" I was slightly puzzled,

"You wanted me" I responded.

Suddenly I heard loud heavy rhythmic thumping on the door, "open up you Jock twat, we know you are in there!"

Shit, I looked at my alarm clock that confirmed it was now one o' clock and realised to my horror that the delightful Chelsea and Becky had appeared for our pre-arranged tryst, and I was now trapped in the room.

My current squeeze was about to quiz me, so I held my hand over her mouth to stifle the noise, while my brain raced to find a solution to my current predicament, which wasn't easy as most of the blood was diverted and occupied elsewhere. The noise they were making beating down the door was inconveniently almost putting me off my rhythm, but I was managing to multi task and kept performing when suddenly I realised Linda's other half Matt was sleeping two doors from me and was surely going to hear the commotion in the corridor. I had no option other than to complete my mission with Linda and then sit it out. I couldn't shout and tell the girls to come back later because that would only confirm that I was in the room and I prayed that Matt was a sound sleeper, because he was quite a big lad and those two cockney twats outside were not getting any quieter.

Eventually they gave up and went off to their room. Unfortunately their room happened to be the one next to mine and also Matt and Linda's room and I had to endure another hour of abuse and banging on the walls. When it went quiet I peered out of the room to check the coast was clear and sneaked Linda silently from my room. I sat on the bed contemplating my narrow escape, then I wondered if my opportunity of playing hide the sausage with Chelsea and Becky had passed me by. "Oh well, nothing ventured, nothing gained" so I went next door to the two sleeping beauties to check if they were still up for it. The first one I shook awake almost bit my head off and screamed a torrent of abuse at me. I took that as a sign, she was probably not in the mood anymore. The other one sleepily opened her eyes and I gently lifted her naked body over my shoulder and escorted her back to my boudoir. The threesome would have to wait.

The shenanigans were not just confined to our hotel, it seemed to be repeated throughout all the hotels in the resort, especially amongst our team. The Girls didn't seem to get involved as much, or maybe were just a lot more discreet. I remember getting one written warning which started "Gentlemen if this concerns you, please take note" then mentioned something about "involvement with female clients" and referred to something about "behaving like a donkey with two dicks!!!" I was a bit put out when every rep handed me their copy of the letter and said "this is for you Mac."

Kaz was a decent looking girl and great fun to be with but I don't remember her falling for too many people. Shaz on the other hand was still more likely to fight you than fuck you and called the shots on how her relationships went. It was always the male reps who seemed to get into bother.

After one late night partying, Stan and Paul the Poseur had been out for so many hours that there was no point in heading home to their hotels, so wee Brian sorted them a twin room in his apartment block for the few hours remaining till dawn. Stan went straight to bed in the room but Paul had been chatting up a fit looking barmaid in the bar next door to the apartments and decided to move in on her. He was a smooth guy and good looking too, so it was no surprise that she was up for some fun, the only issue was that she shared a rented room with a friend and the friend would already be asleep. Paul suggested his room, but she was tentative about this because she knew he was sharing with Stan. "He is not a problem love, if Stan is sleeping you will never wake him, he is the soundest sleeper I have ever known." That seemed reasonable, so she suggested that Paul checked on Stan to make sure he was asleep.

A short time later Paul was standing over Stan's single bed explaining to him that he was supposed to be a "sound sleeper" and could not be wakened, no matter what. Stan nodded his understanding of his role as a good wingman should and Paul returned to fetch his barmaid and escort her back to their room. As she entered she asked again cautiously "are you sure he is asleep?"

"Of course he is" said Paul shouting in Stan's ear and slapping his forehead to emphasise the point. Stan did not stir or even blink, he was as instructed dead to the world.

"Wow he is a sound sleeper" said the barmaid as she removed all her clothing and climbed on the bed parallel to Stan a few short feet away.

Paul disrobed and climbed on top of the barmaid, placing her in the missionary position and prepared to give his performance, when suddenly out of the corner of his eye he spotted a smiling Stan with both eyes wide open. Grinning straight at him. Paul instantly realised he had not thought this scenario all the way through, in his haste to get her back to the room and he was now going to have Stan's voyeuristic eyes on him all the way to the climax.

Paul turned the girls head in the opposite direction to Stan, flipped her into a doggie style position, holding her hair firmly to make sure she didn't turn her head back and mouthed a very deliberate "Fuck off" to Stan. On seeing the girl was facing the opposite direction, and sensing how uncomfortable Paul was with this situation, Stan took the opportunity to roll on his side facing the pair and cradled his head on his bended wrist for a more comfortable viewing.

Paul tried hard to ignore him and continued his rhythmic thrusting motion, but was still very perturbed by the wide eyed Stan. Suddenly to Paul's horror and without any warning, the lady being pleasured beneath him started to get verbal and very loud about his technique. "Oooohh push it harder, ohh that's it, quicker, quicker" Paul duly obliged, encouraged by her response and a frantically, miming gesturing Stan. Then she screamed out to a mortified Paul "spank me, spank me!"

Stan nearly choked stifling his laughter as Paul, who was very uncomfortable with the whole physical violence thing, gently slapped his hand across her buttocks. "No harder than that, Harder!" she groaned. Again Paul slapped her cheeks albeit a little more forcefully. She screamed pleadingly "Harder, Harder!" with that, Stan leaned over and whacked her powerfully across both buttocks as hard as he could as an alarmed Paul stared over at him in disbelief.

"Yes, yes, that's it" she screamed excitedly. So Stan started battering her rapidly with both hands alternately as Paul tried unsuccessfully to stop Stan's flailing arms using his one free hand. This continued as the ecstatic Barmaid bit into the pillow oblivious to Paul and Stan's grappling contest with each other's arms above her. Eventually she reached her conclusion and turned to look over her shoulder at a flustered, smiling Paul and a soundly sleeping Stan on the opposite bed.

Chapter Fourteen

V.I.P

Another late night at the airport and another batch of new arrivals. We were having three days a week of airport transfers and between the seven reps, we had to cover all the flights coming in and leaving from Manchester, Newcastle, Gatwick, Glasgow etc, etc. I never found this routine boring at all because each journey had its differences. Some outbound flights leaving us were very emotional coach journeys on the way to the airport as we said goodbye to new friends and lovers that we probably wouldn't see again, in spite of all the promises that we would never lose touch.

The inbound flights for me were very exciting as it was our first chance to engage with the new arrivals on the coach journey to the hotels and I could always tell from my welcoming speech on the microphone, what type of group had arrived. I would introduced them to the driver of the coach and then ask them to wish him luck as he was due to sit his driving test in a few weeks, whilst the driver was usually flying along the road at ninety miles an hour. I would be dropping the new Billys at the various hotels and apartments we had arranged and I would again be looking for fun groups or individuals that we could use and recruit to help get the atmosphere buzzing or spot where the pretty ones were being dropped for future stealth missions. The reps would leave messages at the airport for each other to make us aware if we had troublemakers arrive from the Gatwick flight or a loud exciting bunch from Manchester and in which location they were.

This was when we would have to be creative with the overbookings and names missed off the rooming lists but it was something we managed to excel at, although tipping each other off meant we were armed and prepared to deal with it. One night I picked up an absolutely fantastic group of six lads from the Dublin flight and had some great laughs on the coach journey from the Airport. I was a little bit jealous as I was not having them for my hotel but instead dropped them at Stan and Kaz's place. I had already selected the one who was destined to be the team captain at the beach party as little Ryan was the most charming and funniest guy I had ever met in my life. He had a little ginger beard and ginger hair as did most of the Irish lads who arrived and they were all resplendent in their Republic of Ireland green football tops, which I think most of them wore daily for the following two weeks.

Ryan was a people magnet as everyone was drawn to him as soon as he spoke with his beautiful soft Irish intonation. He seemed to charm the ladies immediately, with a little sparkle in his smiling eyes as their knicker elastic melted from ten paces away. The one noticeable thing about Ryan that you didn't immediately notice, was that he was only four foot and ten inches tall, which technically meant he was a dwarf. You were so in awe of his personality that it was not really of any relevance until he stood alongside you and you had a perspective of his small stature. It certainly didn't put the ladies off him as the little fucker was a pulling machine and was having a different bird take care of him every night. His mates had cruelly nicknamed him "Inch" because one inch more would have took him over the dwarf qualification height of four foot ten although judging by reports from his female conquests he was not lacking any inches below the belt.

I had met Kaz at the airport and she told me her earlier arrivals from Newcastle were also a very outrageous Party animal type, group of girls and that Stan had left a message at the airport that his pick-up from Glasgow had a crowd of crazy Jocks already half pissed and singing all the way from the arrivals lounge. I could hardly wait to meet them all and get the partying started.

We would occasionally get VIP visitors and these were clearly marked on our new arrivals paperwork, these guests had to be treated 100% correctly without any mistakes. They were usually relatives of the big bosses in the UK or travel agents that could affect our business or journalists that could hurt our reputation. They were also usually deemed off limits for potential shagging partners!

That night Alan the resort manager came walking into our

hotel bar very sombre, as we hosted yet another late night party. He had just came straight from the Airport with the last of the new arrivals from Belfast and marched straight over to Danny and me. He had a very stern and serious tone in his voice as he spoke to us both.

"There is a girl about to walk in here" he said as he gestured to the reception area. "If you shag her, I will sack you on the spot!" he told us both emphatically.

"Is she related to the MD or someone important? I asked.

"No… she is the most beautiful woman I have ever seen and if you shag her no-one in this hotel will speak to you. The lads will hate you because they will want a crack at her, the girls will hate you because they will feel inadequate and jealous. No one will do anything you ask. She is completely entirely off limits. Do you pair of clowns understand that?"

I glanced at Danny and sniggered, "She can't be all that special surely?" as I poured a bottle of beer into the glass I held. The world seemed to stand still as this incredible breath-taking blonde goddess breezed elegantly through the lounge. Every single person stood in silence as we all drunk in the beauty that stood in front of us and my heart skipped a beat and my whole body tingled while I stared open mouthed, oblivious to the fact that I was pouring beer over my hand and arm. I let out an uncontrollable little gasp of air and a murmur when she smiled her perfect beautiful smile and the room filled with sunlight. I was suddenly vaguely aware of Alans voice in my ear again, "Don't even think about it, she's off limits." He forcefully highlighted the point yet again.

It didn't make things any easier for me when I introduced myself to her and took her feather soft hand in mine stared into her deep blue eyes and heard her gentle Irish accent for the first time. I think I may have ejaculated slightly also.

The next three days were absolute torture. I smiled at her now and then and gazed at her unobserved from a distance as I listened to my male Billys discuss their feeble attempts at trying to bed her.

"Yeah I tried to pull her last night but she wasn't interested, she must be a lesbian." Said one mug.

"I danced with her but when I tried to put my hand on her arse, she nearly broke my arm off." said another.

"Fucking amateurs" I thought.

By day four it was unbearable, I felt like Tantalus the Greek mythological figure having to suffer eternal temptation without satisfaction. I recalled Alans words of warning, still ringing in my inner ears and I thought "Oh well, I suppose I could always get another job." By now my confidence had grown since my first feeble days when I arrived in resort and I had no doubts this girl was going to be mine. The cleaners had a little room tucked behind the kitchen and bar area, where they stored the towels and sheets and it also had a long wide concrete plinth, like a breakfast bar which they used as an ironing board.

I approached this blonde heavenly creature standing there

in a tight pair of cut-off denim shorts and a loose vest and asked her if I could have a quiet word in private and I led her by the hand, behind the bar and into the hidden room. I placed her with her back towards the concrete plinth and gently lifted her by the hips to sit on the plinth facing me and edged her knees apart as I moved my face closer to hers.

"I have desperately wanted to get you alone for the last four days" I told her sincerely.

"Well why haven't you then?" she asked. I told her about Alan warning barring me from making a move on her and she was quite astounded and slightly angered.

"Surely it is up to you and me what we do, to be sure, we are grownups after all, so? I was tinking you didn't like me."

Oh sweet girl you could not be further from the truth. I cradled her porcelain face in my hands as I leaned in and kissed her deeply and I was delighted to discover she was a great kisser as she responded just as eagerly. I gently pulled her long blonde hair with my left hand and as her head moved towards that direction, I softly kissed her exposed neck on the other side. She murmured as my hand crept slowly under her loose vest and I lifted it over her head and dropped it on the floor beside us. Her ample breasts were framed by a white bikini top and I leaned forward and kissed them slowly while undoing her clasp at the back with one hand and pulling the bikini top off to join the vest on the floor. She responded by placing her hand behind my head and pulling my mouth down onto her nipples.

I slipped a hand down aiming between her thighs in an attempt to "get my fingers in the till" and suddenly it all came to an abrupt end as my wrist was grabbed in a vice-like grip by her right hand.

"No way, you're only after da one ting… and you'll not be getting it from me!" she emphatically told me.

I had to humbly agree, I was only after the one thing and time was of the essence as she would be leaving in a short while.

"Yeah you are right, I am only after one thing, you are absolutely gorgeous and you can't really blame me for trying. I don't think I am god's gift to women and I would never expect you to be with me if you don't want to be with me, so I totally respect your decision, we can just be friends and put it behind us."

I handed her the discarded garments and kissed her on the cheek, adjusted the loaded weapon in my shorts and left the room. With my dignity still intact, almost.

For the next few days I was pleasant to her and her mate with the small talk exchanged when we met, I didn't ignore them, but I deliberately didn't make a fuss over them. I was in my room later in the week one afternoon, quietly doing a bit of paperwork as everyone else was at the beach, when I heard a knock on the bedroom door. I shouted that it was open and to enter and blondies friend stuck her head in the room and asked if I was alone. On seeing that I was she added;

"Oi have a little surproise for ya" she went back out the door and blondie walked in all seductively, then turned to lock the door behind her and started undressing.

"What's going on" I asked

"I thought you said you weren't interested?"

She looked at me and said "Oi've changed me mind."

I reached over and picked up her discarded clothing yet again and handed it back to her as I leaned in her ear and whispered "no!"

"What?" she blurted out, incredulously.

"No not here" I said, then made her dress and escorted her back down into the hidden cleaners cupboard where I bend her over the plinth and continued our liaison at the point she had paused it a few days earlier.

"You bastard" she laughed, as I released a week's worth of frustration.

My only problem now, was keeping the smug grin off my face in case it alerted Alan to my greatest career achievement so far, and remembering not to do the Morecambe and Wise dance towards the other Reps.

I was falling in love now at least three times a week, sometimes three times a day as I realised how much I could exploit the power of this magic badge and the incredible opportunity this much sought after job had afforded me. I was a very, very lucky boy to find myself in this role as a holiday rep.

Danny on the other hand did not know the meaning of the

word love. Danny did not know the meaning of lots of words but the "L" word was utterly confusing to him. He did not see the point in hanging around after the dirty deed had been done and all interest in that specific liaison was over as the quest for the next notch on the bedpost began.

I had a less direct approach but a more subtle theory that if I gave it my best shot and was the "best lover" they had ever had, then they would tell their friend or roommate. This way the roommate would begin to look at me in a different light, knowing about my hidden talents and I may have an increased chance of servicing them too. Danny could not care less about what they thought or how he rated with them, it had happened and that was all that mattered.

One day a new arrival changed that for Danny, albeit temporarily. Polly had arrived with a couple of friends from Stoke and could hardly wait to get her kit off to sunbathe. She was blonde and pasty white but had a terrific shaped figure and a nice pair of large upstanding boobs. Danny being very much a breast man noticed her on the sunroof with a small glimpse of interest.

By the end of her sunbathing session, she had transformed into a golden brown stunning bleached blonde and turned quite a few heads as she wandered back through the bar. I recognised the look of lust in Danny's eye and was underwhelmed to find out that he had managed to pull her that very night. What was surprising though, was that he had allowed her to stay all through the whole night and then to my astoundment, he spent the next five nights with her until she departed. This required investigation. "Ok Danny boy, what's the story?" I asked, expecting him to admit he had finally found true love at last and that Polly was his dream girl. The real story was quite a distance away from that scenario.

Firstly he admitted that the first night he had made the crucial error of falling asleep and found her lying on his arm in the early morning. Unable to escape the scene he gently nudged Polly to let her know it was time to leave. She wakened and smiled at him, then reached over his shoulder to the bedside cabinet and grabbed a bottle of after sun lotion, which she then squirted all over his sleeping appendage. Within a few moments Danny was standing proud and enjoying the sensation of the lotion being applied in the rhythmic motion. Suddenly Polly stopped and straddled him sitting forcefully down, persuading Danny's aroused member inside her back door. Danny's eyes almost popped out of his head as he let out a surprised "whoa."

Over the next few days she continued to pull tricks out of the bag which kept Danny interested for almost a full week, it was not very often he met ladies who were more experienced than him.

I had a little insight into Polly's world during one of our small group conversations. We could easily be on stage in front of hundreds of people and be in total control, but it was much harder work sitting around a table with just a few Billys on an afternoon having a beer. If the Billys were a quiet bunch, to get the conversation going I would often say; "Tell us about your most embarrassing moment." This usually brought tales of boobs slipping from dresses on a night out or trunks falling down at the poolside. It was a fun way of getting people talking and hearing a few stories, when it was Polly's turn to talk, she went all coy and shy.

"Oh I don't think I should" she giggled.

"Go on Polly, we've all told our stories."

Again she giggled "It's too embarrassing"

I persisted "Come on girl, the stage is yours." I then sat staring in open mouthed amazement along with the others around the table as Polly recounted how she had went out to sea on a pedalo with five guys for a "dare". They had pedalled out far enough not to be seen from prying eyes on the shoreline as she knelt on the Pedalo "accommodating" all five gentlemen at once.

"Shit, you had five guys on you and you were embarrassed about it?" I asked.

"Oh no, it wasn't that, a Hydrofoil boat came past us a few feet away and all the families were looking out the window at me!!"

I still cannot get that mental picture out of my mind and I can't help thinking how rewarding Danny's time spent with Polly must have been, although I had to agree with Danny that she was probably not the marrying kind.

Back at Stan and Kaz's hotel the joint had been jumping all week with the Northern group from Glasgow, Newcastle and

Manchester all adding to the constant party atmosphere. All these areas had a working class backgrounds and they seemed to gel very well together and appeared to be having an absolute blast. It was reported to me that Wee Ryan, was humping proudly for Ireland and was scoring every night, his banter was great as he looked some pretty little girl up and down and exclaimed "oi can see a little bit of me, in you... hopefully later" then with a cheeky wink he was charming his way into someone's bed again.

I think it was the cute vulnerable impression that he gave, that had the girls wrapped around his finger. He had been through most of the Geordie and Glaswegian girls and had been spreading his seed further afield within the surrounding hotels and apartments too. If shagging was an Olympic sport Wee Ryan was earning triple golds.

The beach party was fast approaching that weekend and as usual we had been winding each other up amongst the reps as to who would win the competition. Saturday could not come quick enough for me as it was one of my favourite trips. We would be meeting up at the usual beach bar and travelling from far and wide as we all descended on the much publicised beach party and the carnage that it brought.

I was a little dismayed to find out that Ryan had not come along to the Beach party. Stan told me his mates had not seen him since the Friday night when he disappeared with a couple of scouse girls from one of the local tourist hotels nearby when they had met up at a bar crawl. "The little focker will still be workin' his way thro them Mac, its standard for him, don't worry he'll eventually turn up." Said Sean, one of Ryan's mates, not remotely bothered at all.

We had our usual monumental beach party and returned back late Saturday evening and went our separate ways. On Sunday morning I woke to find a slightly distressed Kaz, knocking on my hotel room door. "Hi Mac, it's probably nothing, but no one has seen Ryan for two nights now. We met the scouse girls last night on our pub crawl and they said he had left early on the Saturday morning to get the bus to the beach party, apparently he was really looking forward to it. We've asked all around the hotel and pubs but no one has seen him."

We gathered all the Reps and as many Billys who could be bothered and started trying to retrace Ryan's steps, searching the beach areas and all the clubs and almost everywhere we could think of, but to no avail. I wondered if he had maybe fell and knocked himself unconscious but by Sunday evening we were still no closer to finding him. Sunday was an airport arrivals and departures day, so I would need to call the reps off the search very soon to man the airport buses but this was developing into quite a worrying situation. I called Alan and we sat in my hotel lounge, discussing calling in the local police and foreign offices when Doctor Juan appeared at the reception and nodded over to me.

I immediately thought Ryan had been involved in an accident and Doctor Juan had realised he was one of ours and had come to break the news. The truth was much worse.

Doctor Juan slowly and a little embarrassingly explained that as he was sitting down for his evening meal with Mrs Juan and Fernando, they noticed Fernando slipping some fruit and chicken into his school satchel. When they asked Fernando what he was doing with the food, he said "it's for my Leprechaun."

Fernando had spotted Ryan in his green football top and his little ginger beard walking home from the Scouse girls hotel at seven am on the Saturday and gleefully decided that this was now his very own little live Leprechaun with the southern Irish accent, and had picked up the violently struggling midget under his arm and locked him in one of the storage rooms in the basement cellar, by the lift that my parents had been trapped in and was feeding him twice a day. When Doctor Juan opened the door to release him, Ryan was going so fucking mental that Doctor Juan considered giving him a sedative. It took both Carlos and Juan to hold Ryan back as he tried unsuccessfully to attack poor Fernando, who kept shouting "He's a leprechaun don't let him escape, he's a leprechaun."

Poor old Ryan thought that he was about to be fucked and used by Fernando, the way he had done to so many females since he arrived. It took a whole lot of beers to convince him Fernando was "not right in the head" and stop him pressing charges.

Chapter fifteen

Warts n' all

Having a Doctor nearby to our hotel was a blessing in disguise for the reps as we occasionally needed re-assurance over some medical matters, when we would experience itching and discomfort in our nether regions. We had a standard joke that if you experienced "Reps Rash" you prayed it was just a sweat rash and nothing more serious.

We were constantly sweating in our groin areas with the intense heat, the sand and the constant routine of being pushed in the pool at every opportunity by the Billys, usually while in full uniform, ready for airport duty. The red patches and blotchy discomfort were often cleared using some prescribed creams, but you would still spend a day or two worrying until the diagnosis was confirmed.

Back in the pre AIDS days of the eighties, we seldom wore condoms and we ignorantly thought AIDS was something you caught in deepest Africa where it was supposed to have originated, or else caught it from Gays. The condoms were only used if the female involved in the sexual activity demanded the wearing of one, in case she got pregnant. We didn't really give that much thought either, because once they flew back home, that was usually the end of the relationship forever. There were the occasional overseas phone calls to hotel reception desks from back in the UK with some distressed female wanting to contact the rep who had put her in the family way, but the receptionists were very well versed to apologise and explain "that Rep" had actually left the company to go travelling to Africa, probably looking for a cure for AIDS one would assume. They never gave our contact details out under the threat of death.

Playing Russian roulette with your unsheathed prize possession was reckless and stupid but we were young, and ignorant so we didn't really look too far into the future, just the here and now. I heard many reports of other Reps and the list of diseases that they had been infected with and poor wee Brian ended up with a lifetime souvenir after someone gave him Herpes, which he only discovered towards the end of the season.

One big occupational hazard was that we all had similar tastes in women and if there was a pretty one, most of the reps would have at least made an attempt to bed her. One day I pulled a slim brunette with a lovely smile called Karen and was looking forward to waving in the face of Paul the poseur as she was living right under his nose in his hotel and I had managed a stealth raid. Before one of the trips as the reps met up for the first time in a few days, Paul ran over to tell us about the previous night and how he had done the dirty deed with a filthy little brunette sexpot called Karen in his hotel. I grinned smugly and asked if she did that little trick with her tongue that she likes and watched his jaw drop as I waved frantically in his face an inch from his nose and confirmed I had been there before him. He was horrified as he realized that he had just multiplied the chances of catching "Reps Rash" by a thousand percent and subconsciously glanced down disconsolately at his crotch area. I heard a small cough and both Paul and I turned slowly around to see a grinning Danny who waved one hand in each of our faces and reported he had been there a full day before me too. Oh Fuck! I immediately booked a check-up for me and Paul with Dr Juan. Karen the serial rep Shagger had been spreading the love amongst us and hopefully nothing else. At times like that I really wished my little head would stop doing the thinking for my big head. One day my luck was sure to run out.

That day came on a normal day that started like any other day. I had a Billy with a sunburned foot and a huge water blister on it that needed attention, so off we went to Dr Juan's office. The blister was duly dealt with and as the Billy left the room, I mentioned to the Doc that I had a little bit of "Reps Rash" and was needing some cream. Dr Juan asked me to drop my pants and had a quick look at the redness in my groin and said "sure no problem" but then swiftly added "What's that?" as he pointed to the base of my penis. Just near the pubic hair, there was a tiny little scab which I assumed was from a little nip in the skin when I accidently caught myself in the zip of my trousers, which most men will have experienced at some point in their lives. I suppose it had been there a week or so and I kept knocking the crust off it every day, but it hadn't concerned me or hurt at all, I never considered it may be anything untoward.

Dr Juan then looked me in the eye and said "it could be a genital wart"

Fuckity Fuck! It never crossed my mind.

Dr Juan began writing on a piece of paper, "look this guy is a specialist friend of mine, I want you to go and show it to him" and with that, he handed me the address and a drawn out map with directions and sent me out the door. I stared at the address in disbelief as I contemplated the bombshell that had just been dropped on me. Was this the payback for all my dirty deeds or was Dr Juan on the "wind up" because of all the late night call outs and aggravation we were constantly causing him? I had visions of me going into the address and flopping my member on the counter, only to be told "Sorry mate this is a hardware store." I wandered aimlessly along the road, shaking my head in disbelief and grinning silently inside, he is kidding me, surely?

A few moments later I was outside the building, looking up at a sign which was clearly marked "Dermatologist, Skin specialist and STD Clinic" Shit! It was for real.

I entered the building sheepishly and passed over Dr Juan's hand written note. The receptionist took the note into the attached clinic and a smiling Doctor came out to escort me into his very sterile looking treatment room. He read the note and gave me a sort off "knowing" look and in broken English told me to get on the treatment couch. It looked like it was obviously used for gynaecological examinations with its stirrups on both sides and he indicated for me to lay on my back and place my legs up in them. This has got to be a fucking wind up? I thought as I stripped my bottoms off and assumed the position, waiting on the inevitable hidden cameraman with his Polaroid. I was oblivious to the irony that it was because of my hobby of examining women's bits that I had earned my current predicament.

He poked and prodded "little Mac" with his surgical rubber clad fingers and then commented to me that he was not too sure if it was actually a genital wart, but he was just going to burn it off anyway as a precaution. "You're fucking what?" I asked panicking. He explained that he was going to use a laser to burn off the surface blemish and also burn a few millimetres deeper, "just in case" there was any roots below.

I felt the sweat pool in my lower back as he turned to face his desk briefly and then turned to face me once again, holding what looked like the biggest syringe and needle he could find. I gulped and accepted my fate, then rolled on my side to present my hair arsed buttocks towards him for the insertion of the very large needle. "No, No" he laughed, as it suddenly became clear that the syringe was destined to be embedded in my rapidly shrinking dick. He chuckled "is, ok. Is just a little prick." It may well be sunshine, but it's my little prick and I am not overly happy about this. Two seconds later and for the first and last time, my cock was in a strange man's rubber clad palm as he administered, not one, but four painful deep injections into the

165

base of my shaft. I was horrified, only half an hour ago, I was in Dr Juan's office because my Billy had a sunburnt foot and now I am at the mercy of this lunatic who is about to turn his laser on me. He pulled the surgical mask over his mouth and turned on the light on his forehead and leaned forward as I suddenly became aware of a deep stinging sensation in my lower regions while the laser started to burn me. It was just about bearable and the same feeling of discomfort as having a tattoo. The Doctor looked up at me as he worked and asked if I was enjoying my time in his country?

"Keep your fucking eyes on what you're working on mate" I had watched many James Bond films and was fully aware of what damage a laser can do and besides that, did he realise the future enjoyment of many females from now till the end of the season was dependent on his skills right now.

I turned my head downwards to look at my bits out of curiosity and saw a tiny little flame flickering where the laser met my skin. I glanced away again hurriedly as no one wants to watch that happening, and suddenly my nostrils were filled with the smell of burgers on a Barbeque and I realised it was my own pork sausage being Barbequed by the Spanish Mr Goldfinger.

There was surprisingly a lot of blood and as the Doctor finished he carefully wrapped some gauze and a bandage, albeit a very small bandage I may add, but still a bandage around my now butchered member. At last my ordeal was over, I foolishly though. I was so glad to be off the couch and on my way out the door that I quickly shook hands with the Doctor, glad to hear there was no charge because I was a friend of Dr Juan and I bolted straight out the door into the main street. I consider myself very street-wise and careful and always aware of potential dangers but in my haste to leave, I had forgotten to look outside first to make sure the coast was clear. Unfortunately it was not, and I stood face to face with three of my Billys who were returning from the beach. They smiled at me in recognition, then glanced above my head to see the sign on the building where I had just emerged from. There was a sick delight on their faces as they turned and sprinted back to the hotel to spread their newly discovered secret.

By the time I arrived back at the hotel, obviously unable to walk quickly due to my impromptu operation, all the Billys were cheering and jeering, fake scratching themselves, clapping and walking sideways and then continued with this barrage and heckling for the next week or so.

Towards the end of the week most people had lost interest in it and it was all but forgotten as they found something or someone else to laugh about, but there was a group of five lads from Leeds who would not let it go. Every time a new batch of arrivals came to the hotel, they would shout "keep away from him he has crabs." It became more irritating than funny, so I decided to end it and teach them a valuable lesson. When you have a good crowd and a fun atmosphere you want to keep the ball rolling into the next week and the new guests, but the same thing can roll on with a bad crowd or bad atmosphere too.

I called the lads together and told them "look lads, I know it's funny, but you will need to stop talking about it, it is getting a wee bit embarrassing."

"Don't come too close, ha, ha we'll catch something" said one of the dickheads.

I hit them with the knockout punch. "I caught something off one of the girls who is still here and I don't want to upset her talking about it."

Their expressions changed immediately and there was a small period of silence as they realised the joke was now on them. I wandered off knowing the fallout it would cause. Later in the day one of them would approach me all chummy and wanting to buy me a beer, before subtly asking "you haven't been with that Welsh bird at all Mac have you?" the penny had dropped that I could have been with one of their conquests and may have then infected them too. There was sheer panic and they all approached me at some point during the day and all received the same response. "It wouldn't be fair to talk about her mate, I never kiss and tell." After a few days of them pleading with me and begging for information, I promised them that I would tell them on their last day at the airport departure doors.

The news of my gruesome experience had spread like wildfire through the camp and I was accosted what felt like every five minutes by little groups of Billys asking me the details of my ordeal and wanting to see the resulting damage. I would initially explain the whole story giving details of the pain from the surgery and then I would reach into my shorts and cover my bits with one hand, leaning on the waist band of the shorts to pull the elastic forward, then with my other hand I would pull the bandage forward to show the savage hole in my shaft and expose the blood covered soaked gauze surrounding it. Usually it resulted in people recoiling in horror and a few yelps or unexpected screams as the full extent of the catastrophe hit them. It actually looked worse than it was and I was hoping it would heal quickly as I still had a lot of missions for its use in the next few months ahead. Eventually it was getting too frequent to explain all the details, so I just responded to requests by pulling back the waistband of the shorts or swimming trunks and pulling back the bandage. It brought the same horrified response.

I was gradually getting my routine back to normal although Danny and the other reps would usually remind me by announcing on the coach journey to the Disco tour, that I would love the hippodrome discothèque because it had a very impressive laser show. Wankers. I decided I had to intervene and took the microphone off Danny and made a speech to my tormentors.

"Ok guys, there is a little rumour going around that I had a special gentleman's operation, I can confirm surgery was carried out and the Doctor has advised me to keep the weight off it, therefore I currently have it on a sling around my neck."

The bus echoed to the sound of giggling laughter, so I continued. "I have a visit scheduled this weekend to see a specialist, well he's not really a specialist, he is a flute player and he's going to show me how to cover up all the holes with my fingers so I can piss straight." More laughter, "I did have crabs once before and a friend told me the best trick for getting rid of them. What you do is you shave one side of your pubic hair and then you rub petrol on the other side into the remaining pubes. You set it on fire and when the crabs run onto the pube free side, you crush them with your clenched fist." The Billys were all cheering and laughing and I had won them back over again.

I mentioned previously that the Airport duty was a time for us to be the ultimate professionals, uniforms had to be pressed and immaculately clean and we had to keep control of our guests both in and out of the place. Many people in the UK still had the opinion we were just yobbos and the gutter press would love any opportunity to involve us in a scandal at an Airport or anywhere else for that matter.

I always made an extra effort to iron my white shirt with the company logo emblazoned across the back, and my bright blue trousers. Then I would polish my sparkling white shoes. I swung my company flight bag over my shoulder and held my company clipboard aloft as I confidently strutted through the airport, martialling my punters and fellow reps towards arrivals and departures.

As we reached the airport the five Leeds lads, ran to the front of the bus desperate to know who had infected me. "Come on Mac, which one was it?" I continued to make them squirm as I said I would only tell them once their bags had been checked in.

We arrived at the departure desks which were pretty busy sorting paperwork for around a dozen flights and there was a good few hundred tourists trying to check their bags in.

I moved over to the far side of the departure lounge facing all these suntanned tourists, very content in the knowledge that I was not going home yet. The boys deposited their bags and excitedly approached me again.

"Please Mac, put us out of our misery, who was it that infected you?" I paused, then told them "It was no-one, I didn't catch anything."

"You absolute bastard, I turned down around three girls because I thought you might have been there," said one,

"I've been worried sick all week you shithead" moaned another.

"There you go lads, don't kid a kidder. You should have let it go when I asked you, let this be a lesson in life for you, don't poke sticks at the big dog."

It seemed cruel but it had to be done. I was in charge again and as Danny often tells me "If you are going to be a bear, be a grizzly bear."

The lads wandered off licking their wounds and laughing at the way they were conned, albeit a bit relieved as well. I waved them through the departure gate and turned to head towards arrivals, when all of a sudden I was accosted again by a group of six girls from our bus, who surrounded me. One of them in a high pitched irate voice said "she says, you have a hole in your Dick! Show us." I said "where the fuck have you been all week, you must be the only people in Spain who haven't seen my dick?" "Yeah but we are going home now and they've all seen it, show us your scars on your dick." They seemed quite adamant and oblivious to the fact that we were standing in the airport departure lounge, with hundreds of tourists in full view. "I can't really show you here girls, it's a bit too public."

"Show us now, we can stand round you to cover you." I was ordered.

We shuffled over to the far wall with me facing the wall and my back to the tourists, with three girls circled round from each shoulder in our own private little huddle. I handed the flight bag to one of them and the clipboard to another and then I suddenly realised this was not going to be as easy as I thought. I didn't have my shorts or swimming trunks with an elastic waistband but instead I had a full belt and zip to undo on my trousers. I unfastened the belt and pulled my zip down, then shuffled my trousers to my knees. Holding them in place by opening my thighs wider to keep the tension around the waist of the trousers. I placed my hand inside my underpants in the same manner I normally did with my shorts and pulled the waistband out, then peeled back the blood soaked bandage to expose the wound.

I never contemplated it may be too much of an unexpected shock for them, but immediately one of them gave out an ear-piercing scream like they do in the hammer house of horror films, which caused all six girls to run off in different directions. The surprise shook me too as I relinquished the grip my thighs had on my trousers and watched in slow motion as my trousers fell to my ankles. I glanced over my shoulder to find a few hundred disgusted tourists looking at the group rep with the company name emblazoned across the back of his shirt, trousers around his ankles and his dick in hand, with six young girls running in opposite directions. They all just shook their heads and tutted, muttering about "that lot" that they had read about in the papers. So much for being professional at the Airport.

Chapter sixteen

The Downward slide

The season was now in full swing and as life threw problems and outrageous situations at me on a seemingly daily basis, my confidence was growing as I swatted these issues casually aside.

I became assured and in total control as the leader within me began to surface. I was the decision maker, the problem solver and the one everyone else looked to in a crisis. I would never again stand in a crowd waiting for someone else to step forward and control the situation, I now surprisingly believed in my own capabilities and would gladly accept the responsibility of my own actions and decisions.

I wasn't arrogant or controlling but I definitely was the one "in control". I was no longer fazed when I was told the flights were delayed by five hours or that the Hotels were overbooked by sixteen bodies, or one of my Reps was in trouble with something or someone. It was now normal everyday life and you couldn't waste energy worrying about it, you could only deal with the situations in front of you to the best of your abilities and hope that was good enough. No one can blame you for trying your best and you can only play with the cards you are dealt.

I stopped looking at these issues as problems and now viewed them as "opportunities" as they were now an opportunity to put something right.

These newly acquired competencies were going to be the foundations of my life skills from these days onward but I never realized at the time how much I was learning.

People are strange, they are weird, wonderful, interesting and completely fucked up, all in equal measures. I have always felt that you can learn more from bad situations than from good ones and that it is better to do something you regret than to regret not doing something. If you "fuck up" you can think "oh shit, I won't be doing that again". That is far better than thinking "I wonder what would have happened if I had done that?" This could apply to relationships, jobs and sporting situations. You will learn from your mistakes, and if you don't shoot you will never score.

I met a lot of people in my later life that reminded me of certain types of characters that I met during my holiday repping days and I definitely came across a few "Dodgy Stan's" over the years.

I liked Stan. He was more confident and self-assured than I was at the time and was always onto some scam to make a few extra quid. He always sailed close to the wind and for someone so early into his twenties, he was a shrewd businessman, always buying and selling something. Over his years of working abroad he would find ways of getting his ill-gotten gains out of the country and past customs control. He would buy a car in the foreign country from some unsuspecting local at a knockdown price and pay them in cash for the purchase. He would then drive home and smile at the custom control officers as he drove off the Calais to Dover ferry and then find some other "sucker" to buy the car at an inflated price back in the UK, again obviously for cash. This way he got his stash of money out of the country and made a tidy profit selling the car into the bargain.

His time working with us came to an abrupt end when Alan the resort manager learned of his latest scam involving the bus company we used for the tours. We used them for Airport transfers and our excursions so we knew most of the drivers. We had negotiated a deal to pay per person on the coach instead of a daily hire price for the coach. The thinking behind this was that if we paid to hire a fifty two seater coach to take us to the "Waterslide Park" the morning after a late night Disco tour, there was a fair chance that ten or twelve people would not turn up due to hangovers or hook ups with guests at other Hotels. We had obviously already charged the Billys for the trip which was not refundable, so if the cost of the trip was £20 which was £10 for the bus and £10 for the Waterside Park and ten people never turned up, we would have a clear £200 profit.

Dodgy Stan had already sussed that Alan would not be on the trip and would re-sell the trip to holidaymakers' out-with the group, that he had met in a pub the previous night. He would have eight or so new faces from random strangers on his bus and gamble on the fact that at least eight or so of his own guests would not turn up for that trip. That way Alan would get the head count of fifty people on the bus and waterslide trip and would pay for this amount, whilst Stan would pocket the eight extra £20 fees from the newcomers. Genius! This eventually proved his downfall and ended his thriving enterprise when one day everyone did turn up for the trip and this was brought to Allan's attention by the bus company.

Stan took his sacking with a nonchalant shrug of the shoulders and sat philosophically in the Taxi with me as I escorted him to the Airport and his final Goodbye flight. We exchanged hugs and backslaps and Stan gave me one more shifty nod of the head and sly wink before opening his holdall to reveal thousands of pounds already converted into sterling from the many pesetas he had acquired. It was like a bank robbers haul, "See you around Mac" were his parting words as he sauntered off to the departure gate totally unperturbed and with his mission fully accomplished.

I have a grudging respect for Stan even though he probably rinsed a few fellow reps along the way and I often wonder where he ended up. Probably Parkhurst or Barlinne Prison I would imagine.

One of my most vivid memories of Stan was coincidentally at the Waterslide Park Trip where he "earned" a few quid. Like the rest of us, he had an eye for the ladies, although if Stan's hands were rummaging through your knickers, there was probably a fifty per cent chance he was looking for your purse. Most of our conquests tended to be with our own "Billys" although there was the occasional passing tourist who strolled too near and got picked off.

While the usual carnage was going on around us at the Waterslides with the "Billys" energetically flying down the flumes, Stan wandered off to the main pool for a more sedate couple of lengths on his own. He swam up and down the quieter lanes near the side of the pool and he swam past a young twenty something dark haired beauty with a beaming smile who was hanging on to the side of the pool at the five foot high level. His eyes met hers as he grinned back at her, so on the return leg he stopped and greeted her with a Spanish hello as he got level with her and stood up in the shoulder high water. Stan was somewhat surprised as the smiling beauty launched herself from the side and flung her arms around his neck and wrapped her legs around his waist. Stan placed his hands under both her buttocks to support her and as the closeness of their faces was almost intimate, he gazed into her eyes as he tried to strike a conversation.

He tried speaking Spanish but got no response, "speak English?" He asked but again to no avail. He tried his schoolboy French and German but she just smiled as they continued the embrace, bobbing slightly in the water. Stan racked his brains on how to progress this further, she was obviously interested in him but he had no idea of where she was from or how he could communicate with her, she just smiled her beautiful smile looking longingly into his eyes.

He glanced up in horror at the side of the pool as the young girls special needs carer leaned over and prised her and Stan apart, giving him a scowl of disapproval in the process.

Stan then had to endure two weeks of the other Reps handing him the stigma of being caught trying to "Finger" a "Special" in the pool.

The Waterslide Park was great fun as we arrived there in our hordes with bubble perms, moustaches and speedos on display everywhere. They had the usual lifeguard type guys stationed at the top of the slides to make sure you only slid down one at a time and waited your turn in the queue. These little mini Hitler's stood arrogantly in their yellow vests and bright red shorts, adorned with their Baseball caps, shades, whistles and walkie-talkies, Issuing orders with the occasional shrill blast of the whistle to keep you in-check. One group of Geordie Lads tried to reason with the Guard about letting them slide down in fours or fives but he was having none of it. The first four Geordies just shoved past him and after a short few seconds came shooting out of the flume at the bottom into the splash pool. There ensured some frantic whistling and shouting and then a scream as we waited at the bottom of the slide for the remaining Georgie lads, but instead the projectile emitting from the flume was a blur of yellow and red followed by a walkie-talkie, whistle and baseball cap as the Mini Hitler splashed down into the pool. It turned out the Geordies were fed up with his orders and decided to get him out of their way.

Whilst Stan was obviously motivated by the money, I was the

total opposite, I just wanted to have a good time and money was not that important. I was so proud to represent this holiday Company and I was having the time of my life so I wanted everyone to feel as happy and elated as me. Paul the Poseur often joked that I slept with my badge on.

I still do not see Money as my ultimate aim in life, sure I would love to be rich but I would rather count my fantastic fun memories than sit and count my money. Life will not be judged on how much money that you leave behind but how much of an impact you made on the world. It was time to be carefree and outrageous I was in a job with perks that most young guys could only dream about. I was the envy of my friends and holidaymakers and I wanted to abuse it and squeeze as much fun out of it as I could. The guys on the trips would be looking at me jealous of my status, they may have a ten inch Willie and Porche at home but over here I was the King.

I was well known around all the bars and restaurants in the resort and it was quite empowering to walk amongst the people of the town with the feeling of god like status.

We had arrivals and departures happening two or three times a week and usually the night before a departure we would be nipping out for a big group farewell meal. We would meet in the bar around seven, have a few drinks and then I would phone the restaurant where we were heading to pre warn them of the expected numbers which could be ninety or a hundred. As we shuffled towards the door, I would occasionally spot a couple still remaining at their table and obviously not joining us for the night out. My experience would tell me that it was because it was their last night and they had usually ran out of money. I would ask the question to confirm that they were financially embarrassed and when they admitted this was the reason I would give them £50 of my own money and a piece of paper with my address scrawled on it and say "look I want you to have a good time with the rest of us and enjoy your last night, so when you get back to the UK you can post a cheque to this address." They were always gracious and promised they would do it immediately they touched down, but in truth I never even checked if they did, I just told my Mum to bank any cheques that arrived. I am sure most people sent them. If you didn't and managed to rip-off your caring sharing Rep, well may Karma bite you on the arse for it someday.

One of our favourite restaurants was "La Cabana" which was so cheap and cheerful it was practically stealing from them. It was always a good place to go for a meal when you were running short of money at the end of your holiday. It was shaped like a barn with lines of tables and benches joined together the whole length of the room, if you could imagine an old school hall dining area with about ten long, long rows of tables covered with the same wipe clean plastic table cover although none of the benches were at the same height level. You could admire the stars in the sky above you if you glanced up through the holes in the roof, but the staff were extremely friendly and every meal was only 450 pesetas. Chicken with chips and salad, pork with chips and salad, beef with chips and salad, I am sure they even had chips with chips and salad. But best of all was the litre and a half bottles of wine they spread all over the tables. The wine was disgusting at first but it was free and it was plentiful. If you finished one bottle and held up the empty they would bring two more to replace it and there was no ceiling (literally), they just kept bringing this shit wine which surprisingly tasted better as the night progressed. There was one young lad who was the waiter and he loved us coming to visit because I always made sure everyone left him a big tip, which probably made him more money than his wages earned him. He was so pleased he started giving everyone shit wine as their change, I had to quickly stop that in case anyone went blind with regular use or consumption.

As the season got busier I had to call Miguel the owner to pre-book our spaces around an hour before so when his patrons finished he could reserve that table for our numbers and our imminent arrival. As we turned the corner to the restaurant looking like a school trip with everyone in lines and behaving themselves for a change we were receiving strange looks from the long queue of people waiting for a table in the restaurant. The reason most probably was that while they were waiting in flip flops, shorts and T-shirts, my lot were dressed in their finest eveningwear as I told them we were going to be dinning in the fanciest restaurant in town and that they should dress appropriately. The girls looked resplendent in their fanciest dresses and some of the lads even sported neckties. I was called a few unmentionable names but they all saw the funny side when they were full of shit wine a few hours later.

On one occasion as we approached the restaurant I heard one

mouthy bitch near the front of the waiting queue complaining loudly about our group and its notoriety "That's those yobbos from the newspapers, at least we will be served and finished before they get in." I watched her face turn purple and her mouth fall open in anger as Miguel the owner appeared at the front door, shook my hand and ushered ninety or so bodies, past her and the rest of the queue and into the Barn. I smiled at her deliberately as I joined my group.

We took over the restaurant and filled half the tables in the room and I made everyone in the restaurant including the strangers already there, filled their wine glasses and stood up at the side of their seats as we performed a massive boat race with both sides of the table, continuing to the next table when the last person was reached.

We had a couple of runs through this which was a great way of breaking the ice with our fellow diners and then Danny and I started the real party atmosphere with a few risky party songs. The whole place was singing and laughing and having a great time till around ten minutes later when I felt a tug at my shirt and glanced around to find the mouthy bitch screaming into my face.

"Tell them to be quiet!!" she demanded.

"Fuck off!!" I replied, smiling.

"Get them to stop singing right now" she commanded.

"Fuck off!!" again I responded. I said "look lady, that guy over there is the Restaurant Owner, go ask him if he wants me and my friends to leave or you and your friends to leave?" her husband managed to restrain her in mid-air as she sprang at me with her claws at the ready and I returned to singing the Yogi Bear song as he dragged her screaming from the restaurant.

Chapter Seventeen

Exception Report

As the days and the weeks past and the holiday season got busier, we had increased responsibilities and more paperwork to do, due to increased numbers of holiday makers and the increased problems this meant. The fun side of repping was the public face of how it was perceived but we had a lot of sensible parts to the role behind the scenes to ensure a smooth, fun holiday experience for the masses. There was planning of airport pick-ups, planning the room lists with who was sleeping where, sorting out monies collected for the trips and sending Exception reports back to the UK.

Exception reports covered "anything out of the exception" or something bad that had happened. Any complaints from Billys, accidents or incidents we had to try and warn the UK office before the complaint letter landed on their desk and that way they were already informed of the matter and ready to take the appropriate action.

We had to report the day a group of rowdy brummy Billys

decided the bus driver was a wanker and threw him off the coach and had one of their own guys take over the bus driving duties. I don't know if he even had a normal licence, never mind a bus operator's licence.

I had a few people wishing to curtail their holiday and return home early, either because they had fell out with their travelling companions or were missing their partner back home. We had a few reports of family deaths back home, which were not fun at all, when trying to console someone as you organised their trip home.

I had one report where a couple of awkward girls just didn't fit in with our crowd and were moaning about everything, the type of sand on the beach, the water in the swimming pools the hotel room, almost everything that they possibly could. One of them decided they should go home so they made up a story about being attacked the night before by some Spanish youths on mopeds, which had never happened in our resort in the whole time we had occupied the place, but they were adamant that we arranged a curtailment to their holiday and flew them back home. I felt angry that they were complaining as there was nothing to complain about and I took it quite personally that they didn't enjoy the holiday, I sent a very comprehensive, descriptive exception report giving every detail of the disruption this pair of clowns had caused. A few weeks later I enquired as to how the UK head office had dealt with it and was extremely disappointed to see that the UK office had offered them £50 each off their next holiday. I was outraged, it was all their own doing, why were they being rewarded? I demanded a meeting with

Alan the resort manager and was taught a very clever commercial lesson. He told me "look Mac, they are complaining and making a fuss and will never use our holiday company again etc, etc. we hear this all the time, but instead of rightly telling them to fuck off, we give them a voucher that means they will both have to book a holiday with us again for next year, so we still actually gain some more money from them. They are a pair of twats but hopefully they will be someone else's twats next year and not ours." What a clever business strategy and a lesson learned that although you may appear to be backing down and losing the battle, you are actually strategically backing off to win the war.

I could handle the Billy's complaints with ease usually, it really was water off a ducks back as we bullshitted, manoeuvred and bought our way out of complaints with offers of free booze or even shagging them if the job required it. I did however come up against a guy one day who was a shop steward and had carefully written down all the points he wished to complain about. Most people complaining have one or two valid points but try to make their complaint more powerful by listing minor grievances alongside it. For example if they don't like their view, they won't simply say that, they will probably complain about the bed and the noise from the bar and the breakfast being poor and then try to mention the view from the room. The secret was to swat these minor issues aside and then make them feel like the big issue was not really that important. I would respond with "the noise from the Bar is usually by all of us out partying and when you are pissed you would sleep on anything, so the bed ain't really an issue. You are usually too hungover to make breakfast and why the fuck are you complaining about the view when you are never really in the room?" they would then glance at each other and say "Yeah I suppose you're right Mac" and I would buy them a beer and we were all friends again. Kaz was the best from our team at defusing a situation like this. Shaz on the other hand would probably have just punched them for complaining.

The shop steward guy was amazing, every time I swatted one problem aside he then referred me back to the previous problem he had written down that I had already tried to swat aside. I was floundering. I asked him for a little while to check things over and get back to him. I then sent Shaz in to deal with him. I don't know if she shagged him or threatened him, but he was no longer a problem.

Another new week and another batch of new arrivals. I loved the buzz of the new arrivals and the excitement of seeing what we had. Were there any extra funny groups or were they all dickheads? Were there any weirdos or oddballs? Most importantly, were there any beautiful women for myself and all the reps to set our sights on, or were they just average?

I would have already scanned the rooming lists to see the ratio of male to female Billys and check out which groups were arriving on which flights. We had on occasions some outliers who were not usually associated with our group, like the time we had a bus full of Irish families who were not told by their tour company that they were actually booking a "group" type holiday and arrived to find some bollock naked Billys charging past reception. Poor Grandma nearly shit her pants. I had to rearrange their accommodation elsewhere pronto. I had also sometimes personally cocked up the rooming lists accidentally, like the time a couple who booked a double bed arrived and were unhappy with their view from the room. They were told I could get them a better view but the room would be a twin, which they accepted gratefully. I therefore decided to upgrade the room of Mr and Mrs Jackson who were arriving later that day, and moved them from a twin room into a double bed at no extra charge. I came down to the lounge later on to find them sitting back to back and not talking. I asked if there was a problem and found out they were actually brother and sister. It is a pity they were not from the deepest Norwich area, they probably would not have complained too much.

It was a thrill to watch everyone arrive and I imagine it must be like a prison yard on the day the new fish were paraded in front of the long term prisoners. Danny and I stood in reception to welcome the transfer buses dropping off the newbies and shook hands and introduced ourselves to everyone, then invited them to attend our "welcome meeting" in the bar a half hour later where we would sign them up for all the trips and good times we had planned ahead. We would fix our sights on our next potential lover in the way a soaring Hawk spies a little field mouse below them and offer to help them carry their suitcases to the rooms. It was not unusual for Danny to have his wicked way with someone between lifting their bags into the room and arriving at the welcome meeting a half hour later. Unbelievable!

I moved towards a threesome group of Nottinghamshire girls and lifted a couple of holdall bags. Cindy and her two mates were smiling the minute they arrived and looked as though they would be great fun. I swung the first hold-all over my shoulder and almost collapsed to the ground because of the weight of it. "Fuck, what have you got in here, is it your whole shoe collection?" Cindy smiled back at me, but offered no answer. As I wandered past the other new arrivals on my way to the stairs I spotted a couple of much older men standing at the back of the new batch. I nodded at them and smiled as I thought they must be taxi drivers or something dropping people off, they can't be with us surely?

I was relieved to make Cindy's room without dislocating my shoulder and gave her an inviting smile as I suggested we had a drink together later on. She smiled back already knowing exactly what I had in mind. I popped back to reception and immediately went behind the desk to check the passports of the newly arrived guests. I found the two old blokes passports on the top of the pile and found out they were merchant seamen, one of which was a mere youngster at 54 years of age, at least in comparison to his friend at 65 years of age.

I caught up with them that afternoon in the bar and tried to find out if they had booked the trip by mistake, they were quite upfront with me in the fact they had a few weeks shore leave due to them and both the dates and the cheapness of the holiday had appealed to them. I suppose if you normally sleep in a hammock, our shit hotel must feel like the Ritz. They wouldn't be coming on our trips and would just be doing their own thing.

I was quite cool with that and told them I was around if they had any problems or questions to help them enjoy their break. I did not foresee any trouble at all from them.

That evening we were going on another local bar crawl and I would be trying to work my charm on Cindy. The first bar we passed at the corner of our hotel was a "British pub". They did full English breakfast, served English ales and was ran by an arrogant knob called Terry. I had met him on my first day in the resort as I walked past his bar for the first time ever and he accosted me.

"You the new rep then?" he continued without waiting for an answer. "You can bring your mob in here anytime during the week except Wednesday or Thursday, I've got darts teams and don't ever bring them in on a Sunday I'm busy, I do Sunday lunches!"

I nodded my acknowledgement of the instructions and walked on. I then made it a point at every welcome meeting I had for the whole season, to point out to my Billys that the British bar at the corner was a no go area, due to the amount of people that had bad stomach cramps because of his dirty beer pipes and mentioned the numerous occasions that the health inspectors investigated his poor hygiene practices. I think Rats had been mentioned once or twice around the kitchen area. I also made sure that as we marched en masse past his door on our pub crawls and saw him lurking at his door, I would tell my 100 or so Billys "Say hello to Terry everyone". "Hello Terry" said everyone as his eyes lit up in anticipation of us entering his premises. Then I said "say goodbye Terry everyone". "Goodbye Terry" shouted everyone at the crestfallen bar owner as we strolled away like a giant centipede giving the arrogant fucker a giant middle finger on a daily basis. By halfway through the season he was begging me to bring them in, but I never did.

We had our usual eventful night in and out of the local Bars and at the end of a very late evening of drinking, we staggered back home only to discover that some of the hotel rooms had been broken into. Unfortunately for Cindy and her mates, their balcony was near to a surrounding perimeter wall, which had obviously aided the thieves' method of entry. I would have to escort the lovely Cindy to the Police station in the morning to obtain a crime report number and fill in yet another new piece of paperwork for me.

I was quite looking forward to some alone time with Cindy, it would give me an opportunity to turn on the charm and make up for the chance that the break-in had denied me of. We had a giggle and a bit of flirting walking up to the Police Station and eventually had to turn our serious faces on as we stood in front of the stern looking desk sergeant as he waited on me translating for Cindy. "He wants to know what was taken."

Cindy gave the list of cameras, watches, money jewellery and I added a few bits to get the value up. Then I remembered the heavy holdall that was now nowhere to be seen. "What was in that big heavy bag Cindy?" I urged her to tell me. "Oh nothing important" said Cindy. Confused I mentioned how heavy the bag was when I had carried it into the room, there had to be something of value inside it. "No nothing at all" she insisted. We filled in the forms and left the Police Station with the crime report number we needed for the insurance documents to pay out and we walked in silence for a few minutes. I was very confused and as I looked at Cindy for an explanation, I could see her shoulders shuddering as she tried to stifle her giggles. "Ok what is going on?" I demanded to know.

Cindy apologised first, then confessed "Mac, I'm into bondage and that holdall held all my bondage gear. There's stiletto heeled boots, kinky underwear, whips, chains and handcuffs, dildos and candles, butt plugs and lube in there. I can't stand in front of the sergeant while you describe all that to him, can I?"

Wow this was exciting, I had never met a girl to my knowledge, who openly practised bondage. I mean what did it actually involve?

All thoughts of a career in bondage started rapidly evaporating as Cindy explained in great graphic detail, what she did with her various lovers, with all these props. I could feel my sphincter muscle tense as she metamorphosed into a dominatrix in front of my eyes and her voice sounded excited as she explained "I carve "I love you" into my boyfriend's chest with my sharpened six inch heels, then I drip candle wax into the cuts" I glazed over in horror trying not to picture the scene as she continued describing where the various props went and into which orifice. "You should try it sometime" she purred invitingly.

"Not a fucking chance" I hinted strongly as I left her at the door of the hotel and then spent the rest of her holiday time with us, trying to stay sober and avoid being left alone with her, in case she had packed some spares in her other bags. She scared me immensely.

I did however have a short discussion with one of her friends on their last day. I had popped back into the hotel from the beach one morning to pick up my sunglasses and found one of the trio sitting in the lounge beside a pile of suitcases.

"You off home today then?" I asked her.

"Yeah, we got kicked out the room at 10.30am and the coach won't pick us up till 8.30pm tonight. We are taking turns at watching the luggage, the other two girls have just gone off to the town for some last minute shopping".

"Did you all have a good holiday?" I asked.

"Oh yes Mac, it was the best holiday we have ever had, we loved the resort but you reps and the trips were amazing, you made it really special for us." She added "The only downside was that none of us got shagged during the whole holiday."

"Really" I said, glancing at her golden tan and then my watch. Being the kind and considerate holiday representative that I was I enquired "What time did you say the bus was picking you up?"

She immediately abandoned her luggage guard job duties and we rectified the only downside to their holiday enjoyment. Ironically I met Cindy at an event later in the year when we had an organised Group weekend reunion, where she pulled me aside and jokingly gave me some grief at being a sneaky bastard. "She told us on the plane on the way home that you shagged her, she was the only one who got any action on the holiday."

"You only had to ask Cindy, I would have shagged all three of you." I laughed, although on reflection the handcuffs would have to be put on Cindy first... she still scares me.

One of the Billys had been laid low with the alcohol consumption and was staying at home that evening feeling a bit sorry for himself while we went out on a trip to a BBQ evening in the mountains. When we arrived back later he was sitting in the lounge waiting for me with a beaming smile and an urgent update. He had popped into the bar to get some bottled water earlier in the evening and as the hotel was empty with us being at the BBQ, he was startled by a noise as he glanced over and saw our old Merchant Sailors leave their room next to his and head off into town. A few hours' sleep later he awoke to hear the familiar noise next door to him that told him the sailors had pulled a couple of birds and were giving them a "proper seeing to" judging by the moans of pleasure and screams from their room. He mischievously thought "they must be a couple of right old ugly slappers" for our pensioner sailor boys to have pulled them.

When you are twenty years old, sixty years of age is ancient relic territory. He decided to go and sit in the bar sipping his water and try to catch a glimpse of the old boys bounty as he was sure they must be a couple of hookers. An hour or so later he sat shocked as both the sailor boys exited the room and waved over to him as they left the room alone, but together. Please insert your own joke about life on the ocean waves and developing a taste for seamen.

Chapter Eighteen

Disco Dancing

The Brits abroad always seem to find trouble, usually because of excess alcohol and it was standard for us to somehow always be involved. as trouble always found us. The organised trips needed a mix of some alcohol, some sort of structured entertainment and then the magic ingredient of the reps infectious personalities. Something as simple as the Disco Tour which in reality was just visiting four Discos in one night, became a proper magical night out.

By the third disco we were usually trying to keep the group together as they started drunkenly wandering in different directions and we were working like a welsh shepherds collie on overdrive herding them back again to get them on the bus and to the next venue. There was the usual mishaps of Billys fighting with other groups of drunken yobbos and my Reps and even my boss, getting into scrapes too.

Alan was beginning to like the alcohol a bit too much. Most of us would drink a little and my personal rule was to only drink in the evenings and never during the day, obviously because our drinks were free it was tempting to abuse the privilege. Alan drinking on the tour was not the issue, it was the fact he was driving to the venues in-between that was the problem. We would often have to pull our coach off the road to help lift his mini from the bushes or storm drains at the side of the road, we even found him upside down, still strapped into the seat on more than one occasion like a stranded tortoise. Every time we rescued him, as soon as the car was back on all four wheels, he was pushing us away and back behind the wheel on his journey once again.

We used to be very inventive in the way we spiced up the Disco visits and we would make things up on the journeys in-between. In between singing the usual "Yogi bear" song and "Woman in Black", we would tell the Billys that the next venue was having a "Back to the 60s Night" and then hand out tubs of hair gel making sure everyone slicked back their hair for our arrival.

One of my favourite wind-ups was to announce to the coach that we were getting free entry into the next discotheque because it was having a "Back to Front night". This brought the obvious question from the group of "what is a back to front night?" I replied "because we have our clothes on back to front" then I quickly followed this with an apology for not telling them before we left the Hotel. "It's ok, I will turn the lights out on the coach and you can swap them around now". I would turn the lights off for a few moments and then quickly turn them on again to catch them all in a state of semi-undress and be met with howls of derision. When everyone was ready they looked as ridiculous as expected with shirts buttoned up the back and zips fastened behind them instead of in front.

I then told them that now as they are facing the wrong way, they would need to walk backwards or else they would be going in the opposite direction. They would all exit the bus en masse and walk backwards past the bouncers on the doors laughing and giggling as they marched into the club. The confused bouncers would look at me and ask what was going on? And I would simply shrug my shoulders and shake my head saying "British tourists" and say I had no idea what was happening.

There was obviously no such thing as a back to front night and we were already assured of free entry to the club. Once again the naïve Billys did not realise, that although it was quite a giggle being dressed back to front at this precise moment, later on when they were pissed out of their tiny minds and staggering towards a toilet scrambling at their front of their crotch trying to find a non-existent zip, it was all too late as their bladder gave up the fight and a warm patch emerged at the area where the zip should have been.

Wee Brian still bears the mental scars from one unforgettable Disco tour that will forever remain on his mind.

We had reached our final disco of the night and as I glanced casually around the room I could see Paul the poseur spinning Discs at the DJs booth, Kaz and Shaz dancing with some "Hill-Billy" type Billys and Danny singing and dancing whilst standing on a table. Over in the opposite corner, there was Stan in deep conversation with Alan who was hanging onto the bar trying to stay upright. A perfectly normal scene as I remember it, the only one missing was Brian who I had already had a quiet word with earlier in the evening. Brian had taken a fancy to one girls from a big group of about ten, who were staying at Danny's and my Hotel.

My experience of such matters had alerted my sensible reps antennae and it was becoming a bit too obvious to the watching public that they were getting a bit closer to each other during the dances and conversations, so I pulled him aside to explain, hypocritically the risks of being too obvious. She was quite a good looking girl with a tasty slim figure covered with skin tight white jeans which showed off her pert buttocks and a crop top exposing her midriff. Obviously we noticed her body before glancing up to see her pretty face, overdone with the heavy makeup and her bubble perm setting the look off to perfection. "Don't make it so visible mate, the gaffer is over there and don't dare snog her in front of anyone. Why don't you take her outside, the bus will be leaving shortly so you better hurry up and work your magic if you're taking her home with you."

Brian smiled at the suggestion and I assumed they had discretely slipped away to lock lips outside. It was imperative that when we announced we were leaving a club that we done a head count and left with the same amount of Billys that we had arrived with. We had a few hitting it off with each other and they had changed buses to be with their new friends, but we needed the same total of bodies before we were good to go.

I was two bodies short. I quickly worked out that it was Brian and his lady friend who were missing and got off the bus to hurry them up.

I spotted a very distressed looking Brian coming out of the club entrance. "Quick Mac, I need some help here" he told me in an emotional and very agitated tone. The flustered little fellow had been out the back of the building snogging away with the girl and both of them were getting a little bit frisky. The liaison progressed into intimate touching and was progressing quite nicely until the horrified young girl realised her monthly cycle had arrived unexpectantly and was now very obvious to the whole world as the once pristine white jeans were now deep crimson around the crotch area.

Brian was running in and out of the club with wet paper towels to help clean up the mess. "Mate you both need to get on the bus sharpish, it's about to leave." I told him as I indicated to the five revving buses with the raucous, restless Billys behind me.

A few moments later a mortified looking young girl walked on the bus with her head facing downwards to the floor, as she shamefully walked the length of the bus to join her group of friends in the back seats, trying not to catch anyone's gaze as she hurriedly moved past the staring group.

Brian then slipped on quietly at the front and sat down discreetly as we signalled the driver to get moving. Unbeknown to Brian and myself at the front of the bus, there was an inquest taking place at the back amongst the girl and her friends who were obviously concerned at the state of their pal. Unfortunately they had taken her embarrassment and tearful demeanour in the total wrong context and began barraging her with questions. "What Happened?... did he touch you?... did he force you?"... Then the big question…"Did he rape you?"

The rapid fire questioning, the shame, the embarrassment and the guilt was all too much as she broke down crying and replied with an emphatic "Yes, He Did!"

This was without a shadow of a doubt a lie. I had known Brian for quite a while now and he really was a gentle and sensible guy, he was perfectly sober and at a night club surrounded by witness and in a privileged position to pick from a few hundred very willing participants if he desired a sexual liaison. It made no sense at all, but I was possibly the only other person with the full facts, details and timescales of the incident apart from Brian and the girl.

The group of girls did not say anything as they left the bus although there were a few "C" words aimed towards Brian as they walked past him. Myself, Danny, Brian and most of the remaining group headed towards the bar nearest our hotel for a few more nightcaps and the girls headed towards the town centre, not as it later transpired, to continue partying, but instead to visit the local Police station where they filed a rape accusation against wee Brian.

Ten minutes later a police car and two angry looking policemen arrived at our hotel looking for Brian, with handcuffs at the ready.

Foreign prisons are not like the holiday camp style prisons we have at home and the thought of the wee fella being thrown in some Spanish hell-hole with hardened criminals as cellmates was unimaginable. He was a good looking boy and would have probably ended up as some Spanish Drug cartels adopted bitch.

By a little stroke of luck one of my more sober Billys had spotted the commotion at the hotel and I quickly pieced together the sequence of events and managed to grab the alleged rapist from the bar and escape through the back entrance of the bar, which hopefully would be the only back entrance wee Brian would have to be concerned about.

We ran like gazelles through the back streets and I felt like we were two fugitives escaping from a chain gang being pursued by sniffer dogs. What an adrenaline rush it was and I could feel my heart beating out of my chest as we fled…and I was innocent, I can only imagine what Brian was feeling.

I took Brian to an apartment of a Spanish lady friend of mine called Anna and kept him hidden there for the next week until the girls had left the resort.

In the morning Alan the resort manager and myself spoke with the accuser girl in person as Alan explained the enormity of what she was actually accusing Brian of. She again broke down in tears and admitted she had made the whole thing up because of the peer pressure from her friends on the coach. We immediately took her back to the Police station and formally dropped the charges.

We obviously gave Brian the message that he was exonerated

but he would still have to remain where he was and out of sight so we did not provoke any further trouble.

I shudder to imagine the turmoil in Brian's mind and stomach as he contemplated the nightmare of the situation he found himself in. As a team of reps we all knew he was innocent and horrified at these false claims but being the supportive, jovial bunch we were, instead of welcoming him back into our loving bosom with words of reassurance and cuddles, we decided instead to buy him a zippered bondage balaclava and christened him the "Badger Rapist" as the discotheque was called "The Set" which is where Badgers live.

All of the night excursions and most of the day ones tended to be fuelled by alcohol, all except for one…The Island Buggy Tour.

We would be packed in groups of five into little four wheeled drive beach buggy style jeeps and head off in convoy to visit various tourist spots and places of interest around the Island. On reflection again, we would probably never pass the health and safety requirements of such a trip in the modern era, but back then if you brought your licence on holiday with you, you were allowed to be responsible for the lives of yourself and four fellow passengers, no matter how reckless your driving skills were.

We undoubtedly had a few minor incidents with jeeps taking the sharp bends of the road too fast and bumping into other vehicles, but no one died usually, so it was deemed a successful mission. We would visit scenic beach areas that were hidden from the normal tourist routes and one particular beautiful lake we called the silver springs. It had the most amazing piercing aqua coloured waters and was surrounded by beautiful green foliage and bright flowers. It could only be accessed by walking around 300 meters through a very, very dark, man-made tunnel that stood just over six feet high and was around two and a half foot wide. The tunnel was actually a little trough that carried water from the lake and spring and was around a foot in depth and came up to your mid-shin.

It was slightly claustrophobic in the tunnel with just the tiniest speck of light in the distance which offered the salvation of an exit point, and let you cling onto the hope of escape at the other end.

We would have to walk through the tunnel in single file and would explain to the Billys that they had to hold onto the shirt of the person in front of them as they waded slowly through the water.

There was always a few extra nervous females who had to be cajoled and reassured that we were safe in our great numbers as we headed into the tunnel in groups of thirty or so, with one rep leading the way in front and one at the back to prevent their escape.

We would wait until we were far enough along the tunnel and the screams and shouts were dying down a bit, when the rep would explain loudly that no-one should be worried about the Rats, because the Rats would be more afraid of us. Somehow this did not reassure anyone. The inference that there may be something else in the darkness of the tunnel beside us, worried quite a few of the guests immensely and this became a cacophony of screaming, when the rep at the front started dropping little bits of crumpled paper into the water at his feet and let the flow of the water drag it behind him, brushing off the legs of the now petrified Billys. Sound of "AAARRRRGHHHH, what the fuck was that" and "something just touched my fucking leg" rang out clearly in the blackness.

We would sometimes pretend that there was a ten foot deep hole, halfway along the tunnel and tell them "when you reach the rep, make sure you take a big step of around two foot long to miss out the drop". We would then remain extremely silent as we walked off further along the tunnel, listening to them screaming "where are you, where's the hole? You bastard"

Another highlight of the excursion programme was the Reps Cabaret night, when the talented, fun loving reps would get the chance to show off, and display some of the entertainment skills that had probably got them the job in the first place. We would have put a lot of time and effort into our cabaret rehearsals to make sure everything would run smoothly, already knowing deep down that it wouldn't. This would be a more elaborate version of the small production that we had performed at our final interview stage and we would have a mix of songs and sketches and lots of wind ups on stage.

It is an amazing feeling to be performing on a stage in front of a welcoming friendly audience and because all of the audience already knew us and liked us, there was no real need to be nervous as we were always cheered onto the stage. It must be nerve-racking to enter a stage performance and not know how you are going to be received, but that was not happening to us.

I have never considered myself a good singer, probably average at best, but the crowd cheered loudly anyway so it didn't really matter. This was long before the days of Karaoke machines and was an incredible experience to look out at the smiling cheering crowd. I sang an old country song "Lord its' hard to be humble" and changed the words to make the song all about Paul the poseur, while he had to stand beside me on stage with his unbuttoned shirt and dark shades looking like a proper poseur. "I can't wait to look in the mirror, cos I get better looking each day" It summed my dear friend Paul up to perfection.

We had a "Watch with Mother" sketch, which was a children's show back in the seventies, where I sat crossed legged on stage in the dark dressed as "Andy Pandy" till the spotlight shone on my face to awaken me from my slumber. Paul stood at the side of the stage narrating the act dressed as "Mother".

I would fumble in my groin area as "Mother" would say "look children, Andy is playing with his balls" as the crowd started laughing I would pull out a tennis ball and smile at the audience. "Oh dear children, Andy only has the one ball, where is your other ball Andy?" we would have already picked one of our hot female Billys to be Looby Lou and she would appear from behind the curtain dressed in suspenders and corset wearing a little gym skirt, with big dollops of rouge on her cheeks and sporting pigtails. Looby Lou would then produce Andy's other ball from behind her back and show it to the audience. "Oh look children Looby Lou has been playing with Andy's balls too." "Show the children what you were doing last night Andy"

I would bend Looby Lou over and deliberately place myself at her rear end, with my hands on both her hips and give the audience a "Benny Hill" type grin.

"That's right children, Andy and Looby Lou were playing leapfrog".

We would continue in this vein for the rest of the act and it was all seaside, postcard saucy humour and nothing too offensive. It seemed to go down well and got the crowd in a good mood for the following acts.

We had a knight rider sketch where Kit the car uses songs on the radio to chat up a hitchhiker. We had a Bolero tribute to Torville and Dean with us prancing about pretending to be on ice skates. Rich Arab piss-takes, in fact anyone was fair game to us.

We had a Two Ronnie's type of newsreaders sketch with Stan and Danny wearing big glasses and shirts with ties, reporting on topical and recent events. "The Buckingham Palace chief physician was called today for Lady Diana who complained that Oral sex with Charles was giving her a sore stomach, the Doctor advised her to try Andrews, she said I have but his makes me sick too."

We would pick a few Billys to be included in the news items "Reports coming in that Mary Smith a Middlesbrough prostitute had a recent appendectomy operation that went wrong, the surgeon stitched up the wrong hole, so now she is making a bit of money on the side." And we made sure our recent events were mentioned.

"Reports of homosexuality amongst sailors at a local hotel are totally unfounded said Mr Dalziel, who claims he falls asleep the minute his feet hit the pillow."

It was all done in great humour and the Billys actually got a buzz, hearing their names being read out.

Occasionally you would get a small group who were a bad crowd and would try to heckle and shout out. You can never really win that type of duel with a person holding a microphone and the way Alan usually dealt with it was by announcing "Ok dickhead, if you think you can do better, you come on stage", he would then hand them the microphone and watch them crumble after a few seconds of people booing them off the stage.

One day the tables were turned when one loud drunk was invited on stage and he took the microphone and was absolutely hilarious as he made up a few stories about when he used to work as an agony aunt for a newspaper and had to answer challenging questions. "Dear Morag, when I was eighteen, I could get an erection and I could hold it in both hands and no matter how I tried, it would not bend in the middle. Now I am eighty, I can still get an erection and hold it in both hands, but now it bends in the middle... does this mean I am getting stronger?"

He also said one guy had wrote in and said "my wife has a clitoris three inches long, is this a record?" He replied "No, but it will take some licking".

These same routines were happening in every resort that the

Group had hotels in, and the reps were doing similar cabaret shows all over the continent. We had some standard sketches and songs that everyone did and one of these was a song about a "Special" cowboy called Boldfinger and sung to the tune of "Ghost riders in the sky". We were all dressed up as cowboys and wee Brian had the highest pitched voice and the role of Boldfinger. We would split the crowded room in half and the ones on the left would shout "Whip" on cue and the ones on the right would shout "lash" when it was their turn.

The verse started "As I rode through the valley, a cowboy I espied ... his trousers round his ankles, round a tree his hands were tied... he told me he been ravaged by an outlaw that was gay, as I unzipped my flies I said" Then wee Brian in a camp voice would sing... "It's not your lucky day!"

Then the crowd joined in..."Yippee IOOO, Yippee IAAA, WHIP... LASH, Boldfingers on my thigh"

"On searching for adventure and running short on dough, I entered as a rider in the local Rodeo.....I grabbed a stallion by the tail and mounted from behind, shouting you can ride him your way......" then Gay Brian "and I will ride him mine".

We had a further few verses and then got ready for our finale which had everyone's arms linked singing New York, New York in a Frank Sinatra style.

The Billys then retired to the bar area to get even more pissed and we collapsed exhausted back stage as the adrenaline and nervous energy left us and we crashed and burned.

It was like receiving a hero's welcome as we eventually made it to the bar and received the plaudits for the show. The elation was like nothing I had ever experienced before and fame became like a drug to us as we strived forevermore to become the star of the show wherever we went. Nerves were now a thing of the past and being shy and retiring would never again be in my nature.

Chapter Nineteen

The Bull Ring

Most mornings I would wake up hungover, put on my positive mental attitude face and be down in time for cornflakes.

There was always something planned for later in the day and even if there was no organised excursion, we would have pencilled in some sort of activity. It was a bit like your school timetable, in the way you had every day ahead memorised.

It may be airport duty to collect new arrivals or a trip to a local beach or a night out having a pizza. Something was always on the go.

Tonight was another of my favourite trips as we visited the Bull Ring to have some "Mock" Bull fighting. It was quite a journey to get there, probably over an hour or more but well worth the hassle. We would arrive at the Stadium where we had organised a pre Bullfight BBQ in the middle of the Bull Ring. The picnic tables were already laid out and the chefs were already slaving away at the hot coals as the beautiful smell of charred meat filled the air.

We would sit quite civilised drinking cheap wine and eating our fill of steak and chicken, slowly letting the alcohol do its job. When we finished eating and as the tables were cleared away from the arena, we would have a sing song right where we stood, usually audience participation songs like "Father Abraham" or "the Music man" anything that would start the party off well. "I am the music man, I come from down your way and I can play... What can you play?... I can play the piano...pia...pia...piano, piano, piano" we had them playing the dam busters theme with arms out wide like an aeroplane and at the time Michael Jackson had recently set his hair on fire while filming a Pepsi commercial, so we would play the Michael Jackson "ooh, ooh my heads on fire, my heads on fire, my heads on fire" whilst they all bounced around slapping the top of their heads.

The Bull Ring Structure is an Amphitheatre with tiered rows of stands that surround a central circular arena on the ground level. This circular area is surrounded by a circular alley where the Bullfighters normally prepare for action and this is separated from the arena by a four and a half foot high wooden wall. There are parts of the wall pushed outwards leaving splits large enough to allow a person through but too small to allow the bull through in case of emergencies. We would place all the Billys in this alleyway circled all around the arena facing the middle as we introduced the Matador into the ring, who was going to give us a demonstration of how to fight a Bull.

The matador was a retired rather rotund old bloke, who in his day must have been a bit of a superstar, fighting these monstrous wild rampaging creatures, but today he would be earning a few quid demonstrating his bygone glory days, entertaining a few hundred drunk British tourists as he fought a "Baby Bull."

The baby bull was about the size of a donkey and to the matador it was like playing with a six week old puppy, as he teased it with his red matadors' cape. To me though, I was aware that the donkey sized bastard still had horns that could hurt me and could run faster than me too.

The matador was a great showman and took his bow in front of the cheering crowd as we let the bull out into the central ring. It flew directly towards the fluttering cape that caught its eye, at a rather fearsome pace and the matador dragged the cape around his body in a circular motion and slapped the bull on its arse as it followed the capes path in a circle around him. He laughed as he toyed with the bull for a further ten minutes, obviously enjoying himself immensely as he relieved his previous glories. Eventually the matador left the ring to screaming applause and adulation.

Alan the resort manager would be compering the whole event on a microphone high in the stands and would announce that we would never ask our beloved Billys to do anything that we ourselves would not do, and that we the Reps would now be taking turns to face the Bull.

Our first volunteer was always Paul the poseur as he loved the limelight and he stepped out carrying the matadors red cape. He was pretty nimble on his feet and managed to keep out of the bulls reach quite easily as it was beginning to tire from its previous exertions with the matador. By the time I took over the cape from Paul the bull was almost knackered.

I stood twenty foot away from the bull waving the red cape wildly and he just stared back at me, snorting. I moved cautiously to around ten foot away, keeping my weight on my back leg for a faster retreat if it was needed. Again the bull just stared at me with no interest in moving at all.

I edged nearer and nearer until I was only a few inches from the bulls nose and waved the cape frantically once more. The bulls big round black eyes just stared back at me and I could feel his snorting breath on my hand as he glared back at me looking completely fed up and confused with the whole charade.

I gave the bull a light slap on the nose expecting him to now try and kill me, but again he just stared at me. I though, this bull is broken, we have completely exhausted the poor thing. I looked around the ring at the crowd spread all around me and shrugged my shoulders in a forlorn acceptance that the show was over and I turned my back to the bull as I decided to graciously walk out of the bull ring, leaving him some dignity. The moment I turned my back, the sneaky fucker decided to bow his head. Point his horns at my buttocks and charge at me.

I ran at full speed towards the wooden four and a half foot wall, with the bulls horns two inches from piercing my arse cheeks the whole distance and I cleared the wall with a foot to spare as I hurtled myself head first over it and into the welcoming bosom of the alleyway, to screams of laughter from the Billys.

We would tell the Billys that they could enter the ring in whatever numbers they liked or go in alone, but only after they had signed a disclaimer that stated if they died or got maimed it was not our fault.

As a further safety precaution we would place a paddling pool in the centre of the ring and fill it full of water then quite deliberately highlight that if the Billys felt they were in any danger at all, they could find salvation by standing in the paddling pool as bulls are frightened of water.

We never really had anyone brave enough or sober enough to enter the ring on their own so they usually entered mob handed, expecting safety in numbers.

When they were in the ring ready for the bull to make its appearance, we would make a slight adjustment without informing the Billys.

We replaced the knackered slow bull with its exceptionally fast, energetic, twin brother.

The bull entered the ring rapidly and headed for the Billys systematically as one by one they fled and headed to the paddling pool. Within a couple of minutes all of the Bullfighting Billys were standing ankle deep in water holding onto each other to stop themselves falling back out. I think we could usually cram in twelve or so Billys to fill the paddling pool. The confused Bull stopped around fifteen foot away, stared at them momentarily before crashing through the centre of the crowd and pool, scattering Billys everywhere like a ten pin bowling strike.

The startled Billys would look upwards to Allan in the stands and scream at him "you said bulls were frightened of water?" Alan would reply "Oh sorry, I thought it was bulls, maybe its cows."

We would then test their gullibility even further by telling them that bulls have poor vision and if you just stand perfectly still, the bull won't touch you as it will think you are a tree. Obviously as the bull got nearer and nearer to them they would realize they had to get out of its way to avoid being mown down because it wasn't stopping. We used the same tricks at every visit to the bull ring without incident until one day we went on the trip with another one of our "Special" Billys.

Sebastian the stutterer had recently arrived at our hotel and was a lovely lad who fitted the "Billy no mates" single share profile perfectly. He had a very noticeable stutter and it was very difficult when chatting one to one to remind yourself to stop trying to finish off his painfully slow sentences for him.

I think the issue for Sebastian was nerves, because when he was pissed, he was perfectly coherent with no stutter at all.

With all my other duties at the bull fight, I hadn't really paid much attention to anyone in particular all evening, until I watched the skinny, frail bespectacled Sebastian, sign the disclaimer and enter the ring, wearing a red t-shirt and a pair of red shorts.

I glanced at Allan "is he winding me up? Red is the only colour you expect the bull to attack." Allan just laughed and shrugged his shoulders.

A few moments later Allan announced his line of "stand perfectly still and the bull won't touch you." Sebastian stood poised looking at the bull charging towards him, almost daring the bull to come at him.

I begged Allan, "Tell him to move, tell him to move." Allan said "Its ok he'll move." I pleaded with him "he won't move, he's fucking stupid."

At that moment the bull smacked Sebastian's legs so hard that he did a full summersault over the bulls body and almost comically landed back on his feet correcting his balance. He glared up at Allan and indignantly berated him. "youuuuu said the bbbbbuuuuuulllll, woo woo would not, tttttttouuuuuccccchhhh meeeee?"

Allan looked directly back at Sebastian and said "Sorry Sebastian, you must have blinked." Sebastian seemed reassured by this news and gave Allan the double thumbs up sign, then stared at the bull with his eyes fully wide open, challenging him as the bull collided with him at full speed once again.

We had a few bumps and bruises with the odd few people, usually the drunks who were unable to react quickly enough and once one of our own coach guides, a beautiful lady called Mariana. Mariana was your typical dumb blonde who stood smiling at all the people around the bull ring alley, not paying the slightest bit of notice to the marauding bull who was charging around trying to maim everyone.

The bull knocked her to the ground but looked more like he was trying to shag her than maim her, a desire that had also crossed my own mind more than a few times. We managed to rescue her but she remained covered in purple and blue hoof prints for the next three weeks.

The crowd standing in the alleyway were having great fun watching the show unfold in front of them and obviously felt secure having the wooden wall between them and the energetic bull. At least they did until we escorted the first bull back into the alleyway beside them and watched as a distressed herd of Billys performed a frantic Mexican wave as the bull came into view beside them and they desperately tried to balance on the top of two inches of wooden fencing, unable to drop to the other side as bull one was waiting there too.

There were views of private places where their suntans had not dared to violate as some of the female Billys lifted their legs higher than they ever thought possible.

One week during our sales pitch to promote the "trips and good times" package for the following fortnight I had spoken excitedly about the Bull fight. One of the new arrivals came over to me and explained that Bulls are a bit stupid and that if you turn their head sideways, they will stop running as the can't see where the ground has gone. I was enlightened by the news but pointed out that it was easier said than done. He laughed and said "but it's only a baby bull."

He was from farming stock himself and I looked at him standing there, over six foot five high with muscle on muscles and big hands like proverbial shovels and asked him honestly "do you think you could do that?"

He assured me it would be no problem. So at the next visit to the bull ring, we announced that Britain's best ever Bullfighter would be taking to the ring for a face-off with the bull.

We built him up and whipped the crowd into a frenzy as the big Dorset Farm lad, entered the ring with the red matadors cape tied around his neck like Superman. The bull foolishly flew towards him and as it got within maiming distance, one big shovel-like hand reached down onto each horn and flipped the bull effortlessly onto its back.

The bull lay still for a moment with all four hooves pointing to the stars, with an expression on his face that said "what the fuck just happened there?"

The big man waved to the crowd and left the ring like a hero as the shamed bull clumsily got back onto its feet.

Sometimes however the result went the other way, one drunken buffoon called Louis, decided it would be funny to try and climb on the bulls back with devastating consequences. The bull was having none of it and threw him to the ground, stamping and goring him with its horns. This idiot had been out drinking all day with some of the locals who had introduced him to the local Spanish moonshine that had now scrambled any reasonable thought processing that he previously possessed.

The bull battered him but we managed to drag him to safety and sat him down to recover. The normal routine after the bullfighting was to then walk the short distance to the nightclub under the stadium which was unsurprisingly called the Bullring Discotheque, but as we walked the short distance to the club, Louis suddenly collapsed on the ground in front of us.

Everyone assumed he was just too pissed to walk straight and had tripped, but Paul was over to attend to him straight away and realised he had actually stopped breathing. There was panic amongst the Billys but Paul luckily knew CPR and tried to revive him as wee Brian ran to the club to phone an ambulance.

By the time the ambulance arrived Paul had somehow brought Louis around and he was sitting up drinking some water. Oblivious to what had just happened. We explained to the Ambulance crew what had occurred but they just looked at each other with an air of "It's just another drunk British tourist ". We struggled to get them to understand the severity of the situation but they still didn't pay us any notice.

We escorted Louis onto the ambulance which was going to take him to the main hospital an hour long drive away, to give him a check over and I climbed in the back alongside him to accompany him. Five minutes into the leisurely journey, his heart stopped beating again and the machinery he was attached to started going crazy. I have never seen the look of panic on anyone, the way it appeared on the faces of the two smug ambulance medics. They immediately pulled the van off to the side of the road and worked frantically shouting and screaming at each other trying to get him breathing again and fighting what increasingly looked like a losing battle, while I sat helplessly, frozen in the corner a few inches away.

After what seemed like an eternity, his heart started beating again and the van continued once more on its journey. We ran every red light and reached the hospital within thirty minutes instead of the scheduled sixty.

I sat for what seemed like forever like a spare part in the hospital waiting room while they tried to stabilise Louis's vitals. The diagnosis seemed to be that he had so much strong alcohol in his system that his brain had seemed to switch off and stop pumping blood from his heart or air from his lungs. They waited until they had pumped his stomach and flushed him through and he had slept a few hours without incident before allowing us to get a taxi back to our hotel around six hours after we had arrived.

The sun had already started to break cover, but I needed to grab a few hours' sleep and got up for a late breakfast around nine thirty. I met a few Billys on the way to the lounge and filled them in about the conclusion of previous night's dramas and then entered the breakfast room to find Louis sitting at his breakfast table with three empty bottle of San Miguel in front of him.

At least I had no worries about any lasting brain damage with Louis as this idiot obviously did not possess any.

Chapter Twenty

End of an Era

Imagine if you can, that you are a world-wide Mega popstar, Film star or sportsman. The male population all want to be you, the female population want to be with you. A party is not a party until you get there and you feel you could practically walk on water.

Every day is an adventure, life could not be better. You're young, fit, popular and hero worshipped by the masses wherever you go. You are practically a God.

Then one day someone says "Thank you very much… But now it is all over."

The season was coming to a close and in the last few weeks the number of Billys was decreasing and every week it seemed another couple of reps would also be saying their goodbyes.

It was emotional, saying goodbye to people you lived and worked with and grew to love and trust (if you don't include Dodgy Stan) for the past six or seven months. I knew from experience that this long goodbye may be the last time we ever saw each other again. We didn't have mobile phones or social media in those days, if you remembered to ask you maybe had their address scribbled on a scrap of paper but it was a terrible realisation that it was over, at least for now.

We still had guests to look after and entertain so I volunteered to stay to the very end along with Allan to tidy up all the loose ends.

It was a tough gig to entertain fifteen or sixteen people but we managed to adjust the trips slightly and the evening meals became more intimate affairs, and we kept the fun factory functioning.

I had never thought about the future, I only lived for the moment but now I had to think what the fuck was I going to do for work or for money and where was I going to live?

Most of the reps, if they had not planned to continue working for the company in the winter ski resorts, the mission was quite straight forward. From the many conquests during the season, a lot of the girls would have initially written to us once or twice before we lost touch. The plan was to contact a dozen or so of these individuals and arrange to visit them for a week during the "off season" one after the other. This way you could pack a rucksack and do a tour of Britain or Ireland revisiting moments of intimacy with the selected harem.

The money you earned from repping and all the commissions would be sitting in the bank untouched and this along with the generosity and hospitality of the ex Billys would give you all you needed to get through the lonely winter months till the next summer season started again.

That on top of the couple of Reunion weekends the company had scheduled, more or less took care of your time, but what about your sanity and expectations.

I found myself back at Mum and Dads unpacking my clothes into my old bedroom that had remained untouched in my absence. It was great to see family and friends and find out what they had all been up to. I also arranged to meet an old friend from the supermarket days at our local pub on Friday.

I got to the pub first and ordered a couple of pints at the bar. As I waited for my drinks, I recognised another old classmate I hadn't seen since leaving school, some six or seven years earlier. He spotted me and came over with a big smile on his face.

"Hi Tommy, how are you pal?" I greeted him.

"Hi Mac, I haven't seen you around for years" he responded. "I've been working abroad Tommy, just got back this week. What have you been up to?"

He Said "I'm married now Mac, do you remember Maureen from our chemistry class? Well I married her, we have three kids now."

I raised an eyebrow "Three kids?" he could only have been about twenty three at most. "Oh that's nice."

"Yeah I have been working at the big factory since I left school and we have quite a nice lifestyle, we go to Blackpool with the kids once a year and usually manage a wee break away in a hired caravan too."

That's great mate, I'm pleased for you" I insincerely responded. I felt a sense of dread because I knew his next question.......

"So what have you been doing then Mac?"

How could I answer that? Well Tommy, I used to spend Thursdays performing on stage for hundreds of people, then go to an all-night Toga party and waken in the morning with a couple of extremely Hot, naked women in my bed. Wednesdays were a bit quieter we used to do a booze cruise all day and then get trashed in the discos all night, then waken in bed in the morning beside some extremely hot naked women in my bed.

Now I am sure Tommy is pretty happy with his lot and I admire him for it. He probably got a nose bleed going as far as Blackpool and I would be amazed if they had ever been abroad. Our locals tended to stay local.

My life was the polar opposite now, I can't stay here anymore in this one horse town, there is a big world out there and I was now equipped to explore it.

I mumbled something about "oh I was just working in Spain for the summer mate, say hello to Maureen from me." And with that I grabbed my two pints and went off to wait for my friend.

I suddenly realised I was a different person now, much different to when I left here and arrived in resort many months before. I was a nice guy, a bit quiet, naïve maybe and not too self-confident. The repping job was not the best paid thing in the world but my goodness, what an education I had earned.

I had saved lives, saved relationships, organised flights, Hotels and buses, took people to hospital, took people to and from police stations, I was a trouble-shooter an organiser, a leader, a character, a shining beacon to people looking for help or looking for fun. I had handled thousands of pounds weekly, I had learned to read people extremely well, manipulate, encourage or even seduce them. I'd faced mental health, mental weight lifters, handled groups of thugs, hordes of screaming hen nights, been a lover an entertainer… I was a fucking legend... and now it had stopped.

The expectations I wanted for my life were not the same as what my friends wanted anymore, people in normal lifestyles do not behave like they do on holiday. How could I go and do a nine to five job with someone telling me where and when to be. The thought was horrific.

I looked across the pub searching for my friend and a little blonde sitting with her friends caught my eye. I flashed her my best smile and rolled my "come to bed" eyes at her. She met my gaze and mouthed back an emphatic "Fuck off" at me, and I felt like an air balloon with a slow puncture. What was happening to me? I was just like everyone else sitting around me. I was nobody special.

When one goes on a two week holiday, I feel the readjustment to normal life takes about a week. You hear them saying "oh this time last week we were…"

The re-adjustment period for me when I eventually hung up my badge permanently, took around a year. I would never trivialise depression, it is a horrible condition that's not always visible. I was not depressed but I was extremely fed up. Life seemed boring. Even now some thirty years later I still long for the opportunity to act crazy, but it is so difficult in this sterile, ridiculous, over politically correct world. People can sue you now for name calling as it offends them. In my day, my Dad told me sticks and stones may break my bones but words can never hurt me.

I don't wish to live the hedonistic life like before, when I was in my twenties. My ageing body could not cope with it for one thing and God knows I don't need another notch on the bedpost or to impress anyone.

Alcohol? These days I can take it or leave it. I did have three months drying out my liver when I first stopped repping but I probably only abused it because it was there, in front of me and free.

But the fame and adulation and fun, that's the drug that I still crave every day.

I found being back at my parents that I didn't really need them to take care of me anymore. I could sew, cook, clean up after myself and make all my own choices and decisions. In fact if I had been double jointed I probably wouldn't even have needed a girlfriend.

I was now very confident about myself and I know there is a thin line between confidence and arrogance, but I am happy to suffer the consequences of my own actions.

I have since had many occasions over the years, when the subject of previous jobs comes up in conversations, mentioned my past employment, which then leads me to holding court at the bar as people demand stories of the wild times they perceived the job entailed. This is the reason for the book as some of the memories are now written down before they do eventually fade from memory.

It is a fine balancing act because people want to know the gory details and listen wide eyed and smiling at the tales initially as they quickly gather around you, but slowly you see their expressions change as they suddenly realise how dull their own lives have usually been in comparison. I even sense that sometimes they feel you are just bullshitting them.

I had to ditch my well-earned collection of saucy Polaroid's that I had carefully gathered as evidence for presenting at our sales meetings. It would be a tough line of questioning explaining to the next girlfriend, why I had a trophy stash of naked pictures of previous conquests. The famous reps badge is still packed away safely in my loft, I just could not part with that and I sometimes glance longingly at it and allow myself a few chuckles at the scrapes it got me into. I doubt I could wear it on a night out in town now and get the same response although I would love to try it sometime and see.

Music still plays an important part in my life and I think most people remember different times and places in their lives when they hear a certain song. There are a lot of songs that remind me of back then and I can easily find my subconscious mind drifting back in time.

I even found myself on holiday in later years with my wife, lined up in the morning waiting with the other Billys in a queue to complain to the hotel duty rep about a dripping tap that kept me awake all night. What a fucking hypocrite, I was telling people to go away when they complained about not having a bed.

For the moment I was going to be working at our company head office in Glasgow answering the phone to travel agents and booking holidays for the next summer season. It was monotonous.

I would pick up the phone to some little travel agents in Sunny Saltcoats and the girl on the other end would say "oh are you new to the office then?"

I would explain I was as I had been working abroad with the group for the previous summer. She would then ask "are you in the new brochure then?"

I was, actually in the new brochure, there were a couple of small pictures of myself and Danny with some Billys in the newly released next summer's holiday brochure. I remember vaguely an official cameraman spending a day lining up the photo shoot. Paul the poseur however was gorgeous and on almost every second page in the brochure, so I told her that I was actually him. I heard her breath escape as she orgasmed slightly over the phone.

From then on whenever that travel agency phoned, I could hear all the wee girls in their office bickering about whose turn it was to speak to me. Thank god they would never come in to the head office and burst their fantasies. Good old Paul still able to make gussets damp from over the phone, I missed the big handsome bastard,

I had only been doing the job a few weeks when I got a random phone call from one of the resort managers of our sister company who ran the "Winter Sun" holidays for older people. They desperately needed an experienced rep who knew the area I had just left and could speak the language, would I be interested?

I was back abroad three days later.

It was a massive adjustment as instead of turning up to work in a vest and shorts, I now had a shirt and tie with light blue trousers and sported the brightest red jacket ever seen. I had two different hotels a mile apart to look after and was allocated set times to be there and deal with the Old Billys and their problems. I had a notice board clearly announcing the times I would be available and a little blank space where I had to put my passport sized photograph.

I didn't get a chance to get my pictures done with the uniform on before I left the UK so I figured I would get it done when I got to resort. The boss mentioned the importance of the picture and explained I would have to travel into the main town to get the pictures done. I didn't have any transport as my hotels were so near to each other so she mentioned that one of the other girl reps would be able to take me as they all had company vehicles.

At that week's sale meeting which was the very next day, I was presented to my new team of reps, who gave me the kind of welcome a Nursery Mothers group would probably give to Gary Glitter. They were so scared of me after hearing who I worked with in the summer and were worried I would have the pensioners doing a naked Congo down the high street. To be fair, I might have done.

I asked each of them individually if they could give me a lift into town using their company cars and individually one after the other, they turned me down.

Rather than just leave the space blank which was unsightly, as I sat in reception during my duty hours that evening, I decided that I would cut a passport sized photo out of a magazine in the hotel reception and fill the gap.

The first face and shoulder sized profile picture I saw, was a colour picture of Idi Amin the former president of Uganda, scowling resplendently in a full military uniform, including his Generals hat, perched at a jaunty angle. It fitted the space perfectly. I had a little chuckle to myself and thought that should bring a few smiles to my wrinkly old Billys on their arrival.

Next morning I came down to meet my new half dozen or so old Biddies, looking sharp in my bright red blazer and light blue trousers with the shirt and tie and even with their cataracts they must have spotted me from three quarters of a mile away. I looked like I had personally put the camp into Butlins.

I entered the hotel reception to find the group of six old women in a circular huddle muttering away and standing just in front of my notice board, clearly stating "Hi, I am Mac, your holiday rep and I will be here between 9 till 10am to answer any questions you may have"

I greeted them with a big beaming smile and a "Hello Girls, are you lovely ladies waiting for me?"

They responded "No son". I said "no I think you are, I can see from the labels on your bags, you are with my company. I am Mac, your holiday rep."

"No son, our rep is a coloured chappie." They replied without smiling.

They were obviously waiting on Idi Amin to arrive and discuss their rooming problems.

Only three days back in resort and I was sitting in front of my new resort manager as she tried to give me a written warning without laughing. "But its fucking funny" I pleaded. "It's unprofessional" she countered, trying hard not to catch my eye.

The "Winter Sun" months ahead with the Wrinkly old brigade (W.O.B.s) was going to present me with more than a few challenges and it eventually transpired that it caused more grief than all of my summer months with the twenty somethings.

But that my friends… is another story.